OKAVANGO RIVER

The flow of a lifeline

OKAVANGO RIVER

The flow of a lifeline

John Mendelsohn & Selma el Obeid

PREFACE

To most people, the Okavango means the Okavango Delta or Swamps: the subject of many books and films that celebrate its wealth of life and beauty. Such acclaim focuses on the fact that the Delta is certainly a special place, and also the biggest wetland in southern Africa. Wetlands regarded as being of international importance are declared as RAMSAR sites, and the Delta is the largest such site in the world. But there is a much wider meaning to the Okavango. This is a river system spanning three countries, where rainfall declines three-fold from the upper catchment to the Delta, and a river that pours about 9.4 cubic kilometres of water into its Delta each year. This, too, is a waterway that flows between a country where life has been cruel for centuries to another country that is now the shining light of development in Africa.

THERE ARE MANY meanings to this river, indeed, and *Okavango River: the flow of a lifeline* is an attempt to explore as many aspects of it as possible. The book was commissioned by the 'Every River has its People Project', a project funded by the Swedish International Development Agency and implemented in Botswana, Namibia and Angola. The project aims to promote the participation of people at all levels in activities and decisions that lead to the wise management of the Okavango River. More specifically, the project distributes information to improve awareness on important processes, issues, constraints and challenges in the Okavango. This book is part of that process. We also hope that by bringing together information from Angola, Namibia and Botswana, the residents of each country will have a better understanding of conditions faced by their neighbours. This is important for an area where water is in short supply and the potential for competition over water resources is thus considerable.

The book draws heavily on a variety of published articles, reports and books, and also on the knowledge of many experts and helpful sources listed below. It is an interesting fact that the quality and quantity of information on the Okavango increases downstream. Major sources of information for the three countries were as follows. Angola: reports and books, the great majority of which were published before independence in 1975, and interviews, field work and an aerial survey we conducted in May 2003. Namibia: information summarized in the recent book *Sand and water: a profile of the Kavango Region in Namibia*. Botswana: staff and reports from the Harry Oppenheimer Okavango Research Centre in Maun, and a large body of published articles and books produced by many scientists and technicians over the years.

Many people and organizations contributed information, ideas, encouragement, assistance and enthusiasm, all of which helped make the production of this book a pleasure. We are grateful for all this support, in particular for the important contributions made by: Shirley Bethune, Patricia Blom, Chris Brown, Helge Denker, Fred Ellery, Nello João, Johan le Roux, Francisco Mandjolo, Jaime Manjinela, Terence McCarthy, Mike Murray-Hudson, João Pessela, Peter and Beverly Pickford, Susan Ringrose, Roger Swart, Cornelis van der Post, Viv and John Ward and Ben White.

In Angola, willing help came from José Antonio, Alessandro Basilico, Frederica Biondi, Calvin, Shelly and Brent Brain, Brendon Carroll, João Baptista Chindandi, Abel Chindele, Laura Cremonini, João Bosco dos Santos, John Hanks, Penelope Howarth, Zakarias Kapilikisa, Leonardo Kulivela, Domingos Lucas, George Murray, Penelope Muteteli, Fanie and Dirk Oosthuizen, Alberto Pedro, Isidro Pinheiro, Bongue Malengue Rodriguez, Tamar Ron, Filipe Sabino, Jimmy Sebastio, Ricardo Tavilla, Lucia Teoli and the Governor and his Office in Kuando Kubango.

In Botswana, we are most grateful to Jaap Arntzen, Hannelore Bendsen, Debbie Gibson, Pete Hancock, Ruud Jansen, Felix Monggae, Don Kgathi, Thoralf Meyer, Innocent Mogale, Dave Parry, Lars Ramberg, Piotr Wolski and the Department of Meteorological Services, Department of Water Affairs, Harry Oppenheimer Okavango Research Centre, Kalahari Conservation Society, Ministry of Minerals, Energy and Water Affairs and Ministry of Works and Transport.

Finally, support in Namibia and elsewhere was kindly provided by Jon Barnes, Brian Bluck, Marina Coetzee, Steve Crerar, Barbara Curtis, Helen de Villiers, Stefan de Wet, Fritz Dittmar, Louis du Pisani, Janice Evans, Maria Fisch, Clinton Hay, Piet Heyns, Werner Hillebrecht, Luise Hoffmann, Brian Jones, Ashley Julius, Marc Lejars, Martin Mendelsohn, Chris Neigh, Terry Newby, Lindsay Norman, Nils Odendaal, John Pallett, Pippa Parker, Sophie Simmonds, Peter Tarr, Beth Terry, Jonathan Timberlake, Compton Tucker, Guido Van Langenhove, Alex Verlinden, Julie Wilk, Agricultural Research Council (South Africa), Earth Satellite Corporation (USA), Namibia Nature Foundation, Namibian Department of Water Affairs, Namibian Meteorological Services, National Archives of Namibia, National Air and Space Administration (USA), National Library of Namibia and University of Maryland Global Land Cover Facility (USA).

JOHN MENDELSOHN & SELMA EL OBEID

A publication for the *Every River has its People Project*

Which aims to promote sound planning and management of the Okavango Basin in support of the mandate and activities of the Permanent Okavango River Basin Commission (OKACOM). Production of *Okavango River: the flow of a lifeline* was funded by the Swedish International Development Agency, and supported by the Kalahari Conservation Society, Namibia Nature Foundation and Harry Oppenheimer Okavango Research Centre. The views and opinions expressed in this book do not necessarily state or reflect those of these organizations.

Struik Publishers
(a division of New Holland Publishing (South Africa) (Pty) Ltd)
Cornelis Struik House
80 McKenzie Street
Cape Town 8001

New Holland Publishing is a division of Johnnic Communications Ltd.

Visit us at **www.struik.co.za**

www.imagesofafrica.co.za
IMAGES OF AFRICA
PHOTO LIBRARY

RAISON
Research and Information Services of Namibia
P O Box 1405
Windhoek
Namibia

First published in 2004
10 9 8 7 6 5 4 3 2

Publishing manager: Pippa Parker
Managing editor: Helen de Villiers
Editor: Lindsay Norman
Design director: Janice Evans
Concept design: Fly Design
Designer: Patricia Blom
Cover design: Patricia Blom

Reproduction by Hirt & Carter Cape (Pty) Ltd
Printed and bound by Kyodo Printing Co (Pte) Ltd, Singapore

ISBN 1 86872 963 X

CONTENTS

OVERVIEW

The Okavango

- Is shared by three countries: Angola, Namibia and Botswana

- Covers an area of about 192,500 square kilometres

- Is home to about 600,000 people

- Has only three urban centres: Menongue, Rundu and Maun

- Ends in the Okavango Delta: the largest freshwater wetland in southern Africa

- Delivers about 9.4 cubic kilometres of water into the Delta each year

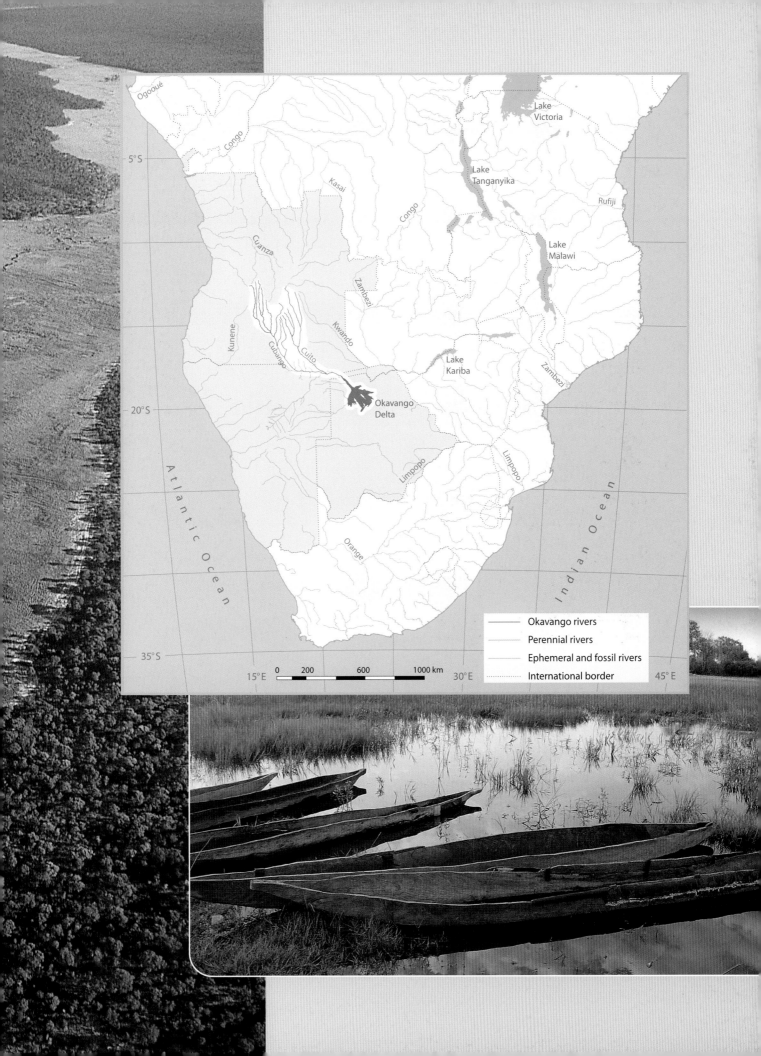

Ogooué

Congo

5°S

Kasai

Cuanza

Congo

Lake
Victoria

Lake
Tanganyika

Rufiji

Lake
Malawi

Kunene

Cubango

Cuito

Zambezi

Kwando

Lake
Kariba

Zambezi

20°S

Okavango
Delta

Atlantic Ocean

Limpopo

Limpopo

Indian Ocean

Orange

35°S

—— Okavango rivers
—— Perennial rivers
—— Ephemeral and fossil rivers
········ International border

15°E   0   200   600   1000 km   30°E   45°E

Landscapes around the river

Most Okavango rivers flow across sandy sediments of the Kalahari, dropping from the highest elevations of over 1,700 metres to the lowest reaches of the Delta at 940 metres above sea level. There is a dense network of tributaries in the north-west catchment where it is hilliest, bedrock is exposed and the mantle of Kalahari sand is thin. Tributaries elsewhere are far apart on a flatter landscape. River gradients become gentler downstream, and a shallow depression caused by rifting confines the final spread of water into the Delta. Most soils in the Basin are sandy and not well suited to crops because of low nutrient levels and poor water retention.

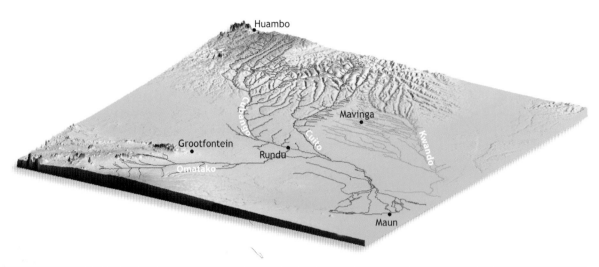

Human footprints

Historically, life in many areas of the Basin has been hard because of disease, warfare, slavery, poor soils and low rainfall. Most people now living here are the descendants of immigrants pushed out of other areas in Angola, Botswana and Namibia. The outside world knew nothing of the Okavango until the mid-1800s. For most of the time since then, however, the Basin has generally been ignored and treated as a desolate area. Angolan society has suffered from centuries of slavery, the recent civil war and corruption.

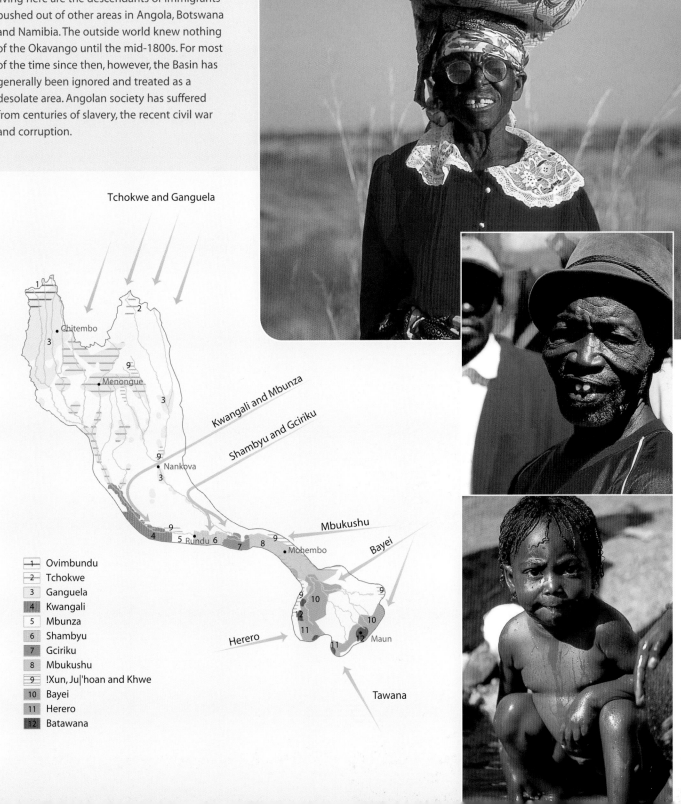

Tchokwe and Ganguela

Chitembo

Menongue

Kwangali and Mbunza

Shambyu and Gciriku

Nankova

Mbukushu

Bayei

Rundu

Mohembo

Herero

Maun

Tawana

1 Ovimbundu
2 Tchokwe
3 Ganguela
4 Kwangali
5 Mbunza
6 Shambyu
7 Gciriku
8 Mbukushu
9 !Xun, Ju|'hoan and Khwe
10 Bayei
11 Herero
12 Batawana

OKAVANGO RIVER

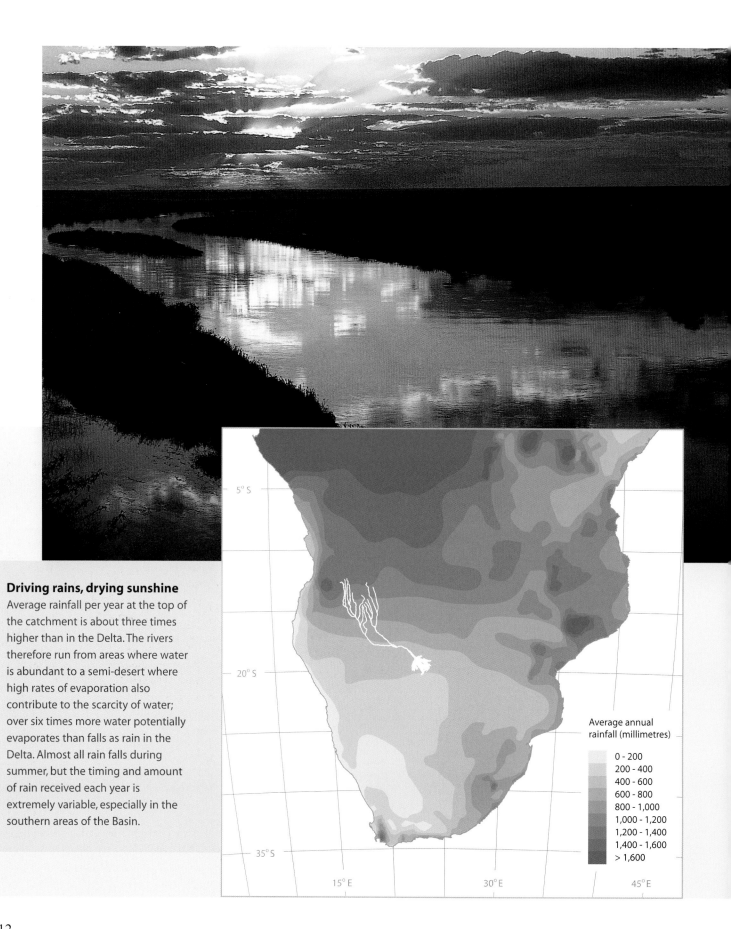

Driving rains, drying sunshine

Average rainfall per year at the top of the catchment is about three times higher than in the Delta. The rivers therefore run from areas where water is abundant to a semi-desert where high rates of evaporation also contribute to the scarcity of water; over six times more water potentially evaporates than falls as rain in the Delta. Almost all rain falls during summer, but the timing and amount of rain received each year is extremely variable, especially in the southern areas of the Basin.

Average annual rainfall (millimetres)

0 - 200
200 - 400
400 - 600
600 - 800
800 - 1,000
1,000 - 1,200
1,200 - 1,400
1,400 - 1,600
> 1,600

Meandering across the Kalahari

All water flowing into the Delta comes from the Angolan catchment, 45% of it down the Cuito and 55% along the Cubango/Okavango. The water is pure and clear because there are few minerals or clay particles in the Kalahari sands and because nutrients are filtered out by plants in the floodplains and marshes along the rivers. However, nutrients that do make their way down the river collect in the Delta, making it very productive biologically. Frequent changes to the distribution of water and habitats in the Delta are due to sand deposition and channels being blocked by plants. Salts in the water become concentrated in soils beneath the Delta as a result of plant transpiration. The size of flooding in the Delta each year depends on inflow from Angola, the degree of flooding in the previous year, local rainfall and evaporation rates.

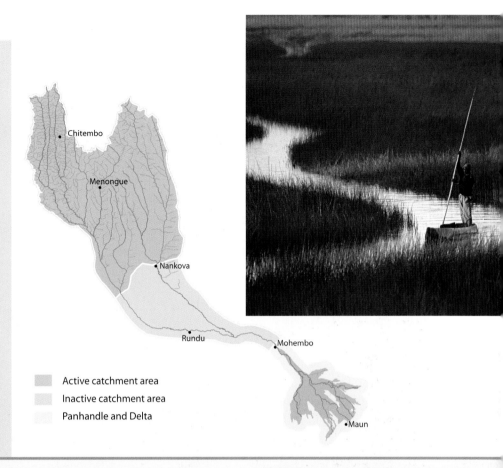

Active catchment area
Inactive catchment area
Panhandle and Delta

Life along the Okavango

Fish stocks are lower than in many other freshwater wetlands because of low nutrient levels. Annual flooding is the main driving force for the breeding of fish. Stocks of fish in the Delta are probably in good health but those in Kavango have apparently declined. Frequent and extensive fires cause the loss of valuable woodlands, pastures and soil nutrients. Baskets, wooden craft, firewood and thatching grass are the most important exports of plant products. Over 200,000 large mammals live in and around the Delta. These animals and other attractions have helped tourism to grow rapidly and earn considerable income in the southern Basin.

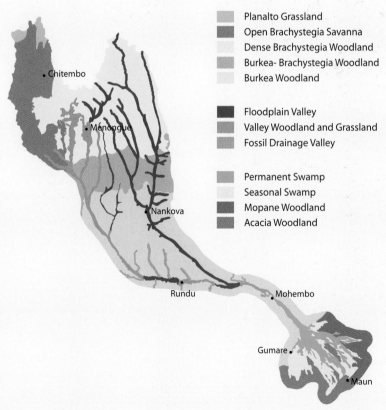

Planalto Grassland
Open Brachystegia Savanna
Dense Brachystegia Woodland
Burkea- Brachystegia Woodland
Burkea Woodland

Floodplain Valley
Valley Woodland and Grassland
Fossil Drainage Valley

Permanent Swamp
Seasonal Swamp
Mopane Woodland
Acacia Woodland

13

Changing and moving people

Approximately 600,000 people live close to the Okavango. Numbers in Ngamiland and Kavango have grown by about 3% each year over the past 90 years, but annual growth in Kavango over the past 30 years has been about 5% because of high rates of immigration from Angola. Other major movements of people have been to large towns or areas outside the Basin. Few functional health and education facilities exist in Angola, whereas most people in Ngamiland and Kavango have good access to clinics and schools. Fertility and mortality rates in Angola are much higher than elsewhere.

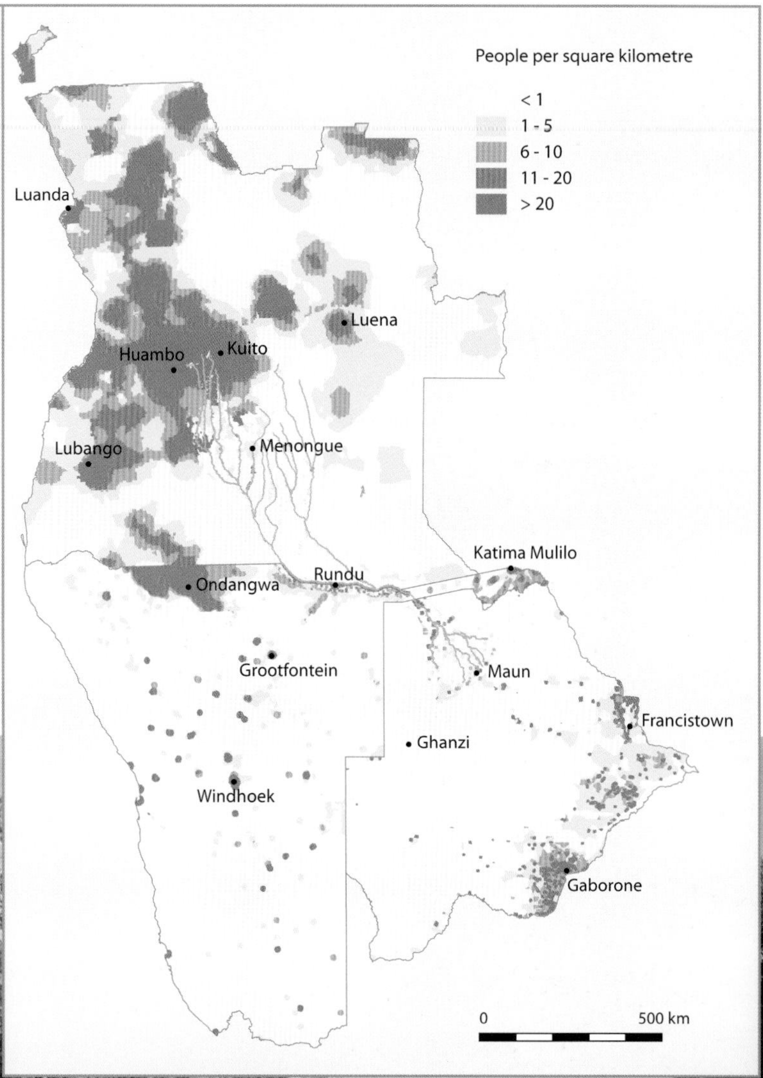

People per square kilometre

- < 1
- 1 - 5
- 6 - 10
- 11 - 20
- > 20

Luanda

Luena

Huambo · Kuito

Lubango

Menongue

Katima Mulilo

Ondangwa   Rundu

Grootfontein   Maun

Francistown

Ghanzi

Windhoek

Gaborone

0   500 km

No cattle
Low
Medium
High

Chitembo
Menongue
Nankova
Rundu
Mohembo
Maun

Chitembo
Menongue
Nankova
Rundu
Mohembo
Maun

Predominantly maize
Predominantly manioc
Predominantly millet
Mixed maize, sorghum and millet

Farming the land

Agriculture is dominated by small-scale crop farming: mainly maize, manioc (cassava), millet and vegetables in Angola, millet in Kavango, and millet, maize and sorghum around the Delta. Most poor subsistence farmers are in Angola, whereas many rural households in Kavango and Ngamiland have cash incomes that far exceed the in-kind value of farming. Yields are higher in Angola than to the south where low and badly timed rainfall makes crop farming unproductive and risky. Livestock farming is progressively more important from north to south in the Basin.

15

Finding your way

The pages ahead provide some guidance for the reader. Names for the different areas are defined on the facing page, followed by two detailed maps of the Okavango Basin on pages 18–21. All places on the maps are listed in a gazetteer on pages 22–23. The book makes frequent use of satellite images – such as the one below – to provide larger perspectives on the Basin. For example, all the rivers and the Delta that make up the Okavango Basin are visible here, as are large areas of land in which trees have been cleared for farming or to harvest wood fuel. The cleared land appears as pale areas surrounding the main towns in Angola, and south of the Namibian border, both along the south bank of the Cubango/Okavango River and in central-northern Namibia.

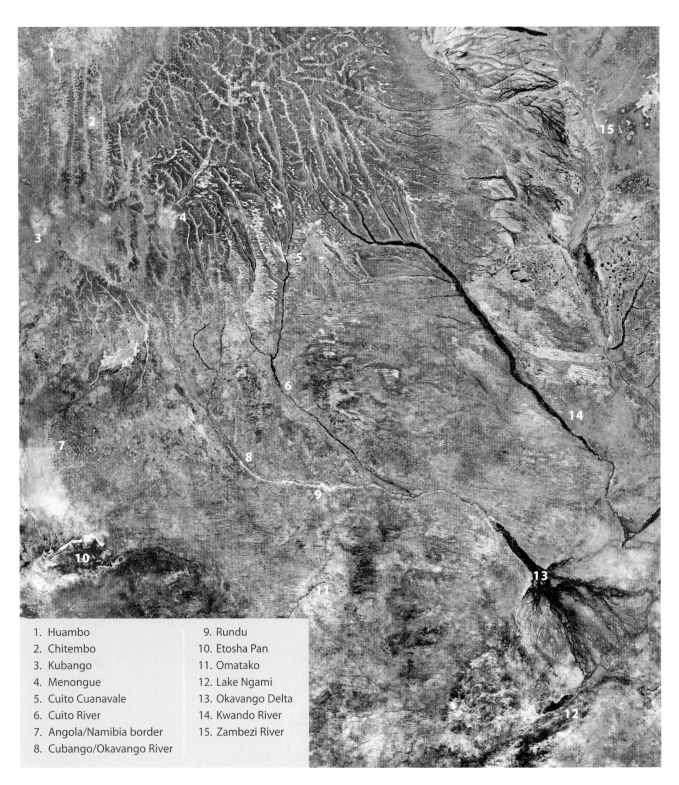

1. Huambo
2. Chitembo
3. Kubango
4. Menongue
5. Cuito Cuanavale
6. Cuito River
7. Angola/Namibia border
8. Cubango/Okavango River
9. Rundu
10. Etosha Pan
11. Omatako
12. Lake Ngami
13. Okavango Delta
14. Kwando River
15. Zambezi River

Figure 1

The Okavango Basin, Cubango and Cuito sub-basins, and the Okavango Delta as defined here. The Okavango Basin covers an area of 192,500 square kilometres, and includes the whole catchment area in Angola, and a zone 20 kilometres either side of the downstream Cubango/ Okavango River and the Delta.

Some definitions

Unless otherwise explained, 'Okavango' refers generally to the whole network of tributary streams, rivers and the Delta in which there is water flow. Surrounding the network is the Okavango 'Basin', which comprises the catchment area from which water actively flows, an additional zone 20 kilometres either side of the Cubango/Okavango River downstream, and the Delta **(Figure 1)**. The 'catchment' of the Basin is limited to Angola where there is active drainage (page 74). Some people choose to define the Basin as covering a much larger expanse that includes the fossil river courses in Namibia, Botswana and Zimbabwe, and also the Makgadikgadi Pans as an area into which Okavango water flowed during much wetter periods. However, these drainage lines do not normally carry water and do not contribute to the wetlands that now make up the Okavango.

The catchment in Angola is divided into the Cubango and Cuito sub-basins as the areas drained by these two major rivers. In referring to the region around the river system in Botswana, we normally talk of Ngamiland because this is the district that encompasses the whole Delta (see page 29). In Namibia, we similarly refer to Kavango because this is the only region through which the Okavango flows. For Angola, however, the river drains areas in five provinces (Bié, Huambo, Huila, Moxico, Kuando Kubango) and the term 'Angola' is used to refer to that part of the Okavango Basin.

Cubango sub-Basin

Cuito sub-Basin

Cubango/Okavango River

Cuito River

Okavango Delta

Legend for maps on pages 18–21

- ▲ Hotel, lodge or safari camp
- ✕ Airport
- ⚑ Border post
- ■ Administrative centre
- • Town or village
- Panhandle
- Permanent Swamp
- Seasonal Swamp
- Marshland
- Perennial river
- Ephemeral river
- Fossil river
- Main road
- Minor road
- Veterinary fence
- Protected conservation area
- Region, district or provincial border
- International boundary

Altitude (metres)

- 900 - 1,000
- 1,000 - 1,100
- 1,100 - 1,200
- 1,200 - 1,300
- 1,300 - 1,400
- 1,400 - 1,500
- 1,500 - 1,600
- 1,600 - 1,700
- 1,700 - 1,800

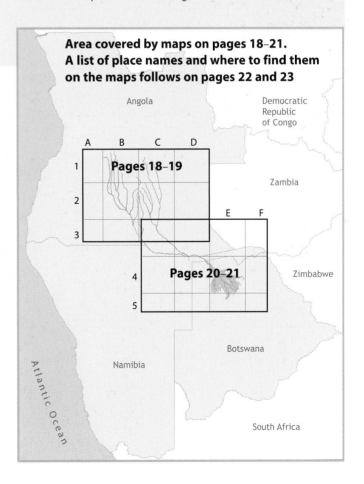

Area covered by maps on pages 18–21. A list of place names and where to find them on the maps follows on pages 22 and 23

Angola

Democratic Republic of Congo

A B C D

1 **Pages 18–19**

Zambia

2

E F

3

4 **Pages 20–21**

Zimbabwe

5

Atlantic Ocean

Namibia

Botswana

South Africa

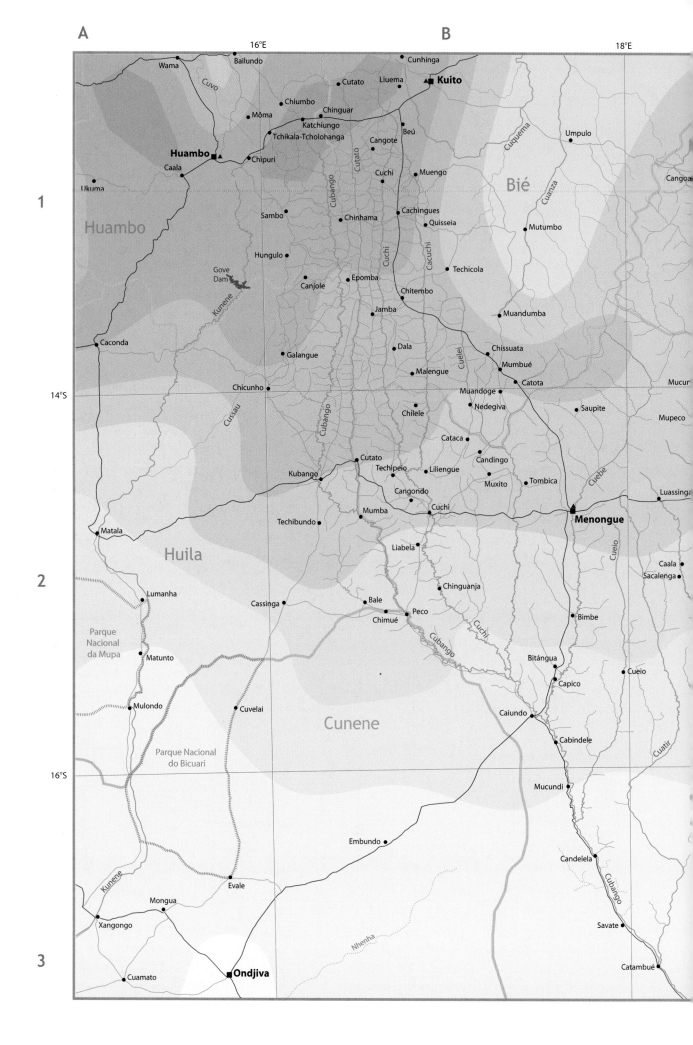

A

16°E

B

18°E

Wama
Bailundo
Cunhinga
Cutato
Liuema
Kuito
Chiumbo
Chinguar
Môma
Katchiungo
Tchikala-Tcholohanga
Beú
Cangote
Huambo
Chipuri
Cuchi
Muengo
Caala
Ukuma

Huambo

Sambo
Chinhama
Cachingues
Quisseia
Mutumbo
Hungulo
Techicola
Gove Dam
Epomba
Canjole
Chitembo
Muandumba
Jamba
Caconda
Dala
Chissuata
Galangue
Mumbué
Malengue
Catota
Chicunho
Muandoge
Mucur
Saupite
Chilele
Nedegiva
Mupeco
Cataca
Candingo
Cutato
Techipeio
Liliengue
Kubango
Muxito
Tombica
Cangondo
Luassinga
Mumba
Cuchi
Techibundo
Menongue
Caala
Liabela
Sacalenga
Chinguanja
Lumanha
Cassinga
Bale
Peco
Bimbe
Chimué

Huila

Bié

Cuito

Cuquema

Cuanza

Cangoa

Cuchi

Cacuchi

Cuelei

Cuebe

Cueio

Cuatir

Cubango

Cubango

Kunene

Cussau

Cuvo

Cutato

Cubango

Cuchi

Parque Nacional da Mupa
Matunto
Bitángua
Cueio
Mulondo
Cuvelai
Caiundo
Cabindele

Cunene

Parque Nacional do Bicuari
Mucundi
Embundo
Candelela
Kunene
Evale
Mongua
Savate
Xangongo
Cuamato
Ondjiva
Catambué
Nhenha

14°S

16°S

1

2

3

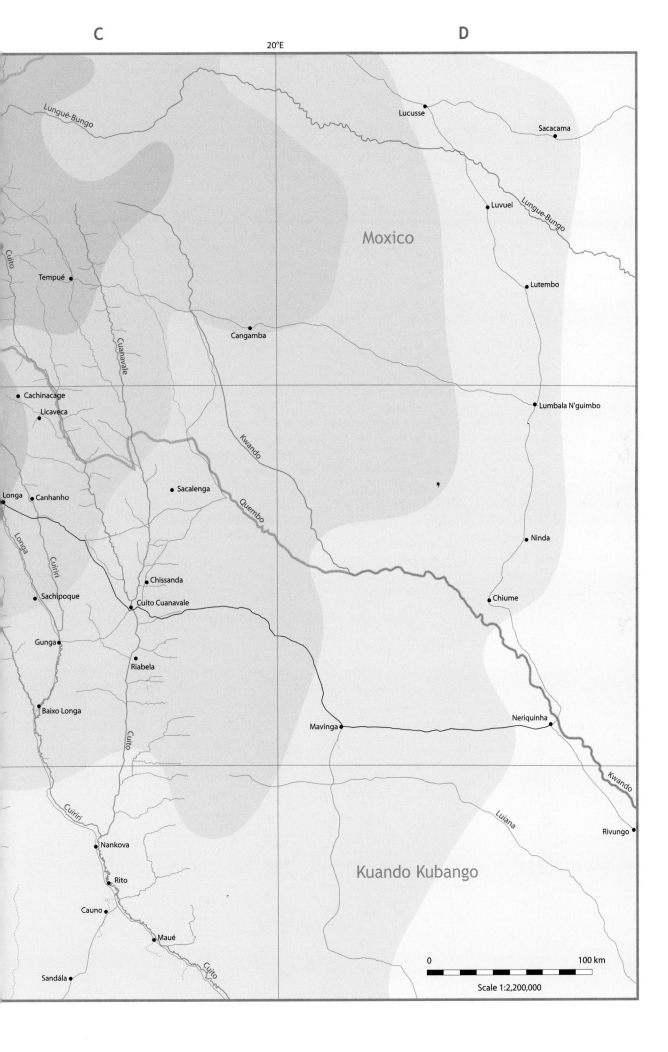

C

D

20°E

Lungué-Bungo

Cuito

Tempué

Cuanavale

Cachinacage

Licaveca

Longa

Canhanho

Longa

Cuiriri

Sachipoque

Gunga

Baixo Longa

Cuito

Cuiriri

Nankova

Rito

Cauno

Maué

Sandála

Sacalenga

Kwando

Quembo

Chissanda

Cuito Cuanavale

Riabela

Cangamba

Moxico

Lucusse

Sacacama

Lungue-Bungo

Luvuei

Lutembo

Lumbala N'guimbo

Ninda

Chiume

Mavinga

Neriquinha

Kwando

Luiana

Rivungo

Kuando Kubango

0   100 km

Scale 1:2,200,000

19

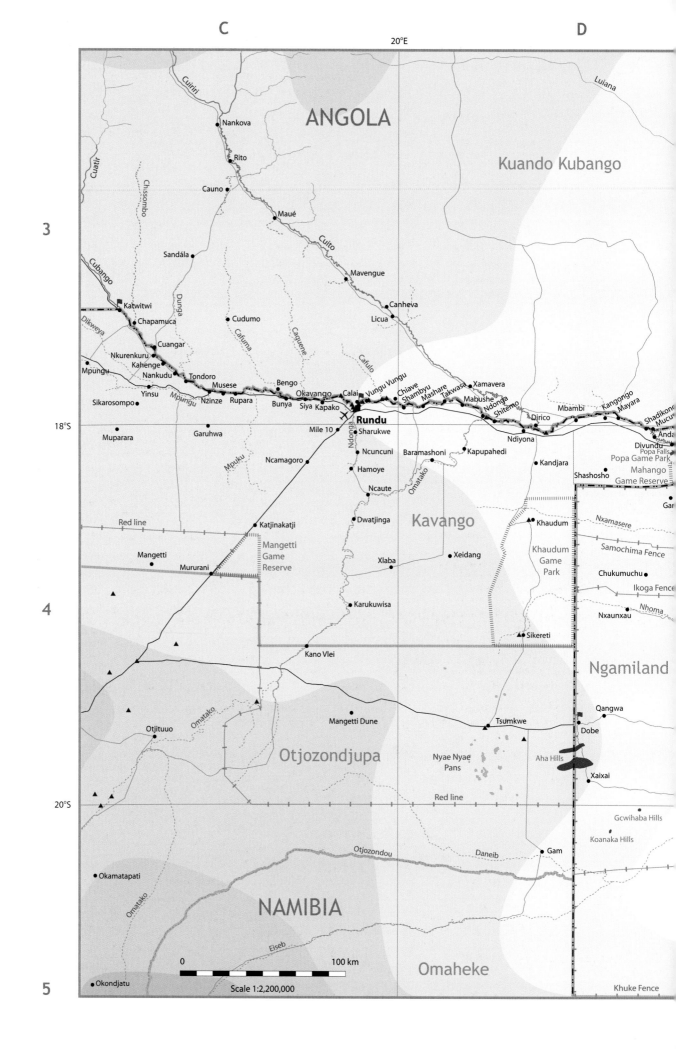

C   20°E   D

ANGOLA

Kuando Kubango

Cuiriri
Nankova
Rito
Cuatir
Cauno
Chissombo
Maué
Cuito
3
Sandála
Mavengue
Cubango
Canheva
Katwitwi
Licua
Chapamuca
Dunga
Cuangar
Cudumo
Nkurenkuru
Cafuma
Kahenge
Caquene
Mpungu
Nankudu
Cafulo
Tondoro
Musese
Vungu Vungu
Xamavera
Bengo
Chiave
Takwasa
Yinsu
Okavango
Shambyu Mashare
Mabushe
Sikarosompo
Mpungu   Nzinze   Rupara
Calai
Ndonga
Kangongo
Mayara
Bunya
Siya Kapako
Shitemo
Mbambi
Shadikone
18°S
Rundu
Ndiyona
Dirico
Mucu
Muparara
Garuhwa
Mile 10
Sharukwe
Anda
Ncamagoro
Ncuncuni
Baramashoni
Kapupahedi
Divundu
Popa Falls
Hamoye
Kandjara
Mahango
Mpuku
Omatako
Shashosho
Game Reserve
Ncaute
Gar
Katjinakatji
Dwatjinga
Kavango
Khaudum
Nxamasere
Red line
Mangetti
Game
Reserve
Xlaba
Xeidang
Khaudum
Game
Park
Samochima Fence
Mangetti
Mururani
Chukumuchu
Ikoga Fence
4
Karukuwisa
Nhoma
Nxaunxau
Sikereti
Kano Vlei
Ngamiland
Otjituuo
Omatako
Qangwa
Tsumkwe
Dobe
Mangetti Dune
Otjozondjupa
Nyae Nyae
Pans
Aha Hills
Xaixai
20°S
Red line
Gcwihaba Hills
Koanaka Hills
Okamatapati
Otjozondou
Daneib
Gam
NAMIBIA
Omatako
Eiseb
0   100 km
Omaheke
Okondjatu
Scale 1:2,200,000
Khuke Fence

20

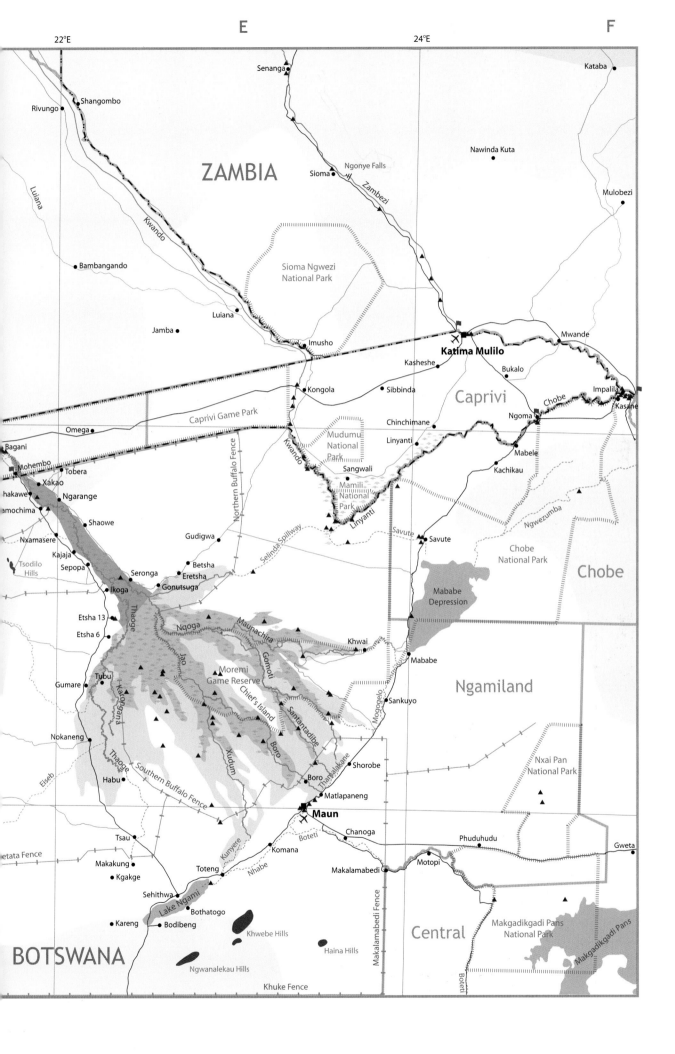

E

F

22°E

24°E

ZAMBIA

Rivungo

Shangombo

Senanga

Kataba

Luiana

Nawinda Kuta

Bambangando

Kwando

Sioma

Ngonye Falls

Zambezi

Mulobezi

Jamba

Luiana

Imusho

Katima Mulilo

Mwande

Kasheshe

Bukalo

Impalila

Kongola

Sibbinda

Caprivi

Ngoma

Chobe

Kasane

Omega

Capriv Game Park

Chinchimane

Linyanti

Mabele

Bagani

Mudumu
National
Park

Kachikau

Mohembo

Tobera

Kwando

Sangwali

Xakao

hakawe

Ngarange

Mamili
National
Park

Northern Buffalo Fence

Ngwezumba

amochima

Shaowe

Linyanti

Savute

Nxamasere

Gudigwa

Selinda Spillway

Savute

Chobe
National
Park

Chobe

Tsodilo
Hills

Kajaja

Sepopa

Betsha
Eretsha

Seronga

Nqoga

Maunachira

Khwai

Ikoga

Gonutsuga

Mababe
Depression

Etsha 13

Thaoge

Mababe

Etsha 6

Jao

Moremi
Game Reserve

Gonoti

Mogogelo

Ngamiland

Gumare

Tubu

Katonqana

Chief's Island

Santantadibe

Sankuyo

Nokaneng

Kudum

Boro

Nxai Pan
National
Park

Thaoge

Southern Buffalo Fence

Thalakane

Shorobe

Habu

Boro

Eiseb

Matlapaneng

etata Fence

Tsau

Maun

Chanoga

Phuduhudu

Gweta

Kunyere

Boteti

Komana

Makalamabedi

Motopi

Makakung

Nhabe

Kgakge

Toteng

Central

Sehithwa

Lake Ngami

Bothatogo

Makgadikgadi Pans
National
Park

Makalamabedi Fence

Makgadikgadi Pans

Kareng

Bodibeng

Khwebe Hills

BOTSWANA

Ngwanalekau Hills

Haina Hills

Boteti

Khuke Fence

21

Gazetteer

Name	Ref	Name	Ref
Aha Hills	D - 4	Chinguar	B - 1
Andara	D - 4	Chinhama	B - 1
Bagani	D - 4	Chipuri	A - 1
Bailundo	A - 1	Chissanda	C - 2
Baixo Longa	C - 2	Chissombo	C - 3
Bale	B - 2	Chissuata	B - 1
Bambangando	E - 3	Chitembo	B - 1
Baramashoni	D - 4	Chiumbo	B 1
Bengo	C - 3	Chiume	D - 2
Betsha	E - 4	Chobe River	F - 3
Beú	B - 1	Chukumuchu	D - 4
Bimbe	B - 2	Cuamato	A - 3
Bitángua	B - 2	Cuanavale River	C - 1
Bodibeng	E - 5	Cuangar	C - 3
Boro Channel	E - 4	Cuanza River	B - 1
Boro village	E - 4	Cuatir River	C - 2
Boteti River	E - 5	Cubango River	B - 2
Bothatogo	E - 5	Cuchi River	B - 1
Bukalo	F - 3	Cuchi town	B - 2
Bunya	C - 3	Cuchi village	B - 1
Caala	A - 1	Cudumo	C - 3
Caala	C - 2	Cuebe River	B - 2
Cabindele	B - 2	Cueio River	B - 2
Cachinacage	C - 2	Cueio village	B - 2
Cachingues	B - 1	Cuelei River	B - 1
Caconda	A - 1	Cuiriri River	C - 2
Cacuchi River	B - 1	Cuito Cuanavale	C - 2
Cafulo drainage	C - 3	Cuito River	C - 1
Cafuma drainage	C - 3	Cunhinga	B - 1
Caiundo	B - 2	Cuquema River	B - 1
Calai	C - 3	Cussau River	A - 2
Candelela	B - 3	Cutato River	B - 1
Candingo	B - 2	Cutato town	B - 2
Cangamba	C - 1	Cutato village	B - 1
Cangoa	C - 1	Cuvelai	A - 2
Cangondo	B - 2	Cuvo River	A - 1
Cangote	B - 1	Dala	B - 1
Canhanho	C - 2	Daneib drainage	D - 5
Canheva	C - 3	Dikweya drainage	C - 3
Canjole	B - 1	Dirico	D - 4
Capico	B - 2	Divundu	D - 4
Caprivi Game Park	E - 3	Dobe	D - 4
Caquene drainage	C - 3	Dunga drainage	C - 3
Cassinga	B - 2	Dwatjinga	C - 4
Cataca	B - 2	Eiseb drainage	D - 4
Catambué	C - 3	Embundo	B - 3
Catota	B - 1	Epomba	B - 1
Cauno	C - 3	Eretsha	E - 4
Chanoga	E - 5	Etsha 13	E - 4
Chapamuca	C - 3	Etsha 6	E - 4
Chiave	C - 3	Evale	A - 3
Chicunho	B - 1	Galangue	B - 1
Chief's Island	E - 4	Gam	D - 5
Chilele	B - 2	Gane	D - 4
Chimué	B - 2	Garuhwa	C - 4
Chinchimane	F - 3	Gcwihaba Hills	D - 5
Chinguanja	B - 2	Gomoti River	E - 4
		Gonutsuga	E - 4
		Gove Dam	A - 1

Name	Ref	Name	Ref
Gudigwa	E - 4	Longa town	C - 2
Gumare	E - 4	Luassinga River	C - 2
Gunga	C - 2	Luatuta-Capango River	C - 3
Gweta	F - 5	Lucusse	D - 1
Habu	E - 4	Luiana River	D - 3
Haina Hills	E - 5	Luiana village	E - 3
Hamoye	C - 4	Lumanha	A - 2
Huambo	A - 1	Lumbala N'guimbo	D - 2
Hungulo	B - 1	Lungue-Bungo River	C - 1
Ikoga Fence	D - 4	Lutembo	D - 1
Ikoga	E - 4	Luvuei	D - 1
Impalila	F - 3	Mababe	F - 4
Imusho	E - 3	Mababe Depression	F - 4
Jamba	B - 1	Mabele	F - 4
Jamba	E - 3	Mabushe	D - 3
Jao Channel	E - 4	Mahango Game Reserve	D - 4
Kachikau	F - 4	Makakung	E - 5
Kahenge	C - 3	Makalamabedi Fence	E - 5
Kajaja	E - 4	Makalamabedi	E - 5
Kandjara	D - 4	Makena	D - 4
Kangongo	D - 3	Makgadikgadi Pan	F - 5
Kano Vlei	C - 4	Malengue	B - 1
Kapako	C - 3	Mamili National Park	E - 4
Kapupahedi	D - 4	Mangetti Dune	C - 4
Kareng	E - 5	Mangetti Game Reserve	C - 4
Karongana Channel	E - 4	Mangetti	C - 4
Karukuwisa	C - 4	Mashare	D - 3
Kasane	F - 3	Matala	A - 2
Kasheshe	F - 3	Matlapaneng	E - 4
Kataba	F - 3	Matunto	A - 2
Katchiungo	B - 1	Maué	C - 3
Katere	D - 4	Maun	E - 4
Katima Mulilo	F - 3	Maunachira Channel	E - 4
Katjinakatji	C - 4	Mavengue	C - 3
Katwitwi	C - 3	Mavinga	D - 2
Kauxwhi	D - 4	Mayara	D - 3
Kgakge	E - 5	Mbambi	D - 3
Khaudum Game Park	D - 4	Menongue	B - 2
Khaudum	D - 4	Mile 10	C - 4
Khuke Fence	D - 5	Mogogelo	E - 4
Khwai	E - 4	Mohembo	D - 4
Khwebe Hills	E - 5	Môma	A - 1
Koanaka Hills	D - 5	Mongua	A - 3
Komana	E - 5	Moremi Game Reserve	E - 4
Kongola	E - 3	Mpuku drainage	C - 4
Kubango	B - 2	Mpungu drainage	C - 3
Kuito	B - 1	Mpungu village	C - 3
Kunene River	A - 1	Muandoge	B - 2
Kunyere Channel	E - 5	Muandumba	B - 1
Kwando River	C - 2	Mucundi	B - 3
Lake Ngami	E - 5	Mucunha	C - 2
Liabela	B - 2	Mucusso	D - 4
Licaveca	C - 2	Mudumu National Park	E - 4
Licua	C - 3	Muengo	B - 1
Liliengue	B - 2	Mukwe	D - 4
Linyanti River	E - 4	Mulobezi	F - 3
Linyanti village	F - 4	Mulondo	A - 2
Liuema	B - 1	Mumba	B - 2
Longa River	C - 2	Mumbué	B - 1

This book makes abundant use of photographs taken from an aeroplane flying several hundred metres above the ground. The three examples below show how qualities and features that may not easily be seen on the ground become clear when viewed from the air. Tracks and paths worn by animals provide a sure sign that wildlife is abundant, as is the case in the Oka-vango Delta (left). People in Menongue do not have access to robust building materials, and thus many people use rocks to hold down corrugated iron roofing sheets on their houses (centre), while termite mounds show up clearly as white spires on a burnt floodplain on the banks of the Cubango River near the town of Kubango (right).

1
INTRODUCTION
The flow of a lifeline

A channel snakes its way across the
Okavango Delta's permanent swamps.

THROUGHOUT THE WORLD rivers flow down to the ocean where their fresh waters mix with salty seawater. This is all due to gravity and the shape of the continents. Imagine, however, a large river that has its fresh waters finally mingle not with salt, but with dry sand in the centre of a flat surface extending about 2,000 kilometres north to south and approximately 1,000 kilometres east to west. This is the Okavango – one of Africa's great rivers. And the sandy landscape is the Kalahari – one of the largest expanses of sand in the world.

But there is much more to the Okavango than a mix of sand and water. This is a river system that collects all its water over a catchment of about 112,000 square kilometres, flows for hundreds of kilometres down a narrow waterway and then finally disperses across a delta covering up to 12,000 square kilometres. Remarkably, the whole catchment is within one country (Angola), the narrow waterway runs through a second (Namibia) and the Okavango Delta lies in a third country (Botswana). The Delta is really a gigantic sink into which the river pours about 9.4 cubic kilometres of water each year. Sediments and nutrients are also carried down from the catchment and they too come to rest in the Delta. The climate is dry around much of the southern half of the river where evaporation rates are six times greater than annual rainfall. But water in the Delta remains sweet, unlike the saline waters prevalent in this arid part of the Kalahari. Compared to most other rivers, the Okavango's water is exceptionally clear of mud and contains few dissolved chemicals or solutes. Environmental conditions along many of the waterways are pristine: natural plant life remains intact in most places, dams or channels do not change the flow of water, and pollutants are scarce. Its size and setting in the semi-arid Kalahari make the Delta perhaps the largest oasis in the world. Along much of their length the rivers of the Okavango system are also linear oases, providing water and food to people, livestock, fish, birds, plants and countless other beneficiaries of this lifeline.

These are some of the key elements of the Okavango. The river system also has high value, especially for two quite different groups of people. The first consists of international tourists and other people who treasure wild places, beautiful scenery and healthy environments. The massive concentrations of wildlife in and around the Delta have made it a highly attractive destination for wealthy visitors. The second group is comprised of people who live close to the river system from which they obtain such resources as water, fish, building materials and jobs in the tourism industry. The substantial importance of these resources

Scrolled patterns mark the remains of sand banks progressively deposited along the meandering Cubango/Okavango on the border between Angola and Namibia (below). Cuttings in sand banks such as these provide nesting places for carmine bee-eaters. The colourful birds lay their eggs in rounded chambers at the ends of the burrows (right). A gourd is a useful container for this boy to carry water home from the Cuebe River in Angola (below left).

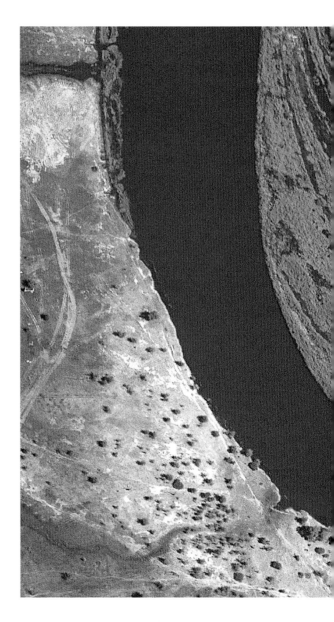

is best appreciated by considering the exorbitant cost of replacing them from alternative sources.

People who benefit most from the Okavango are thus mainly local inhabitants and wealthy people who live elsewhere in the world. The river means little to the majority of people living in Angola, Namibia and Botswana. Most citizens live far from the river, and the Okavango is geographically remote from centres of government and decision-making in all three countries. The development of people close to the river has therefore been ignored for much of the time. Most economic activity and development has taken place away from the river. Resources found in the Okavango's rivers do not compare to wealth to be had from diamonds in north-eastern Angola, in southern Botswana and Namibia, from oil along the Angolan coast, or from fish resources on the Namibian coast.

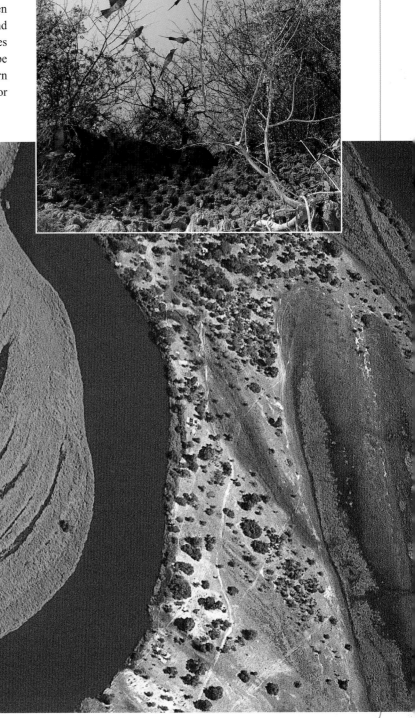

The Okavango provides many resources: nutrients for dense stands of papyrus (above), *fish for white pelicans and other birds* (right), *and water for livestock and people living nearby* (below).

These hard facts are neatly put in a nutshell by the Portuguese description for south-eastern Angola – *as terras do fim do Mundo* – the place at the end of the earth. It is from this remote, wild place that all Okavango water springs. It is an area that has suffered the ravages of war and corruption. It is also the part of the Okavango where rainfall and, therefore, water is plentiful. Rainfall declines and water gains in value to the south. No other open water is available near the river in Namibia or Delta in Botswana, and the Okavango's waters are therefore much more important to these two countries than to Angola. In essence, the Okavango means quite different things to different people and holds different values for these three nations. Material in the pages ahead should shed more light on the workings and many meanings of the Okavango.

Administrative aspects

Angola is divided into 18 provinces **(Figure 2)**. A Provincial Governor administers each province and has considerable authority over all local affairs, including the allocation of funds for the development and maintenance of services. Each province is further

- ■ National capital
- ● Regional capital
- —— Region, district or provincial border
- ········ International boundary

Figure 2

Angola, Namibia and Botswana are, respectively, divided into provinces, regions and districts for purposes of local administration. Those administrative areas across which the Okavango flows are highlighted and the regional capital of each area is shown on the map. Most of the catchment area lies within Kuando Kubango, but the Okavango also drains parts of Moxico, Huila, Huambo and Bié. Menongue, Rundu and Maun, as the three major towns in the Basin, are important administrative and economic centres. All three are more than 250 kilometres away from any other large towns.[1]

There may be as many as 60,000 lechwe in the Delta, making this the most abundant large mammal in the Okavango Basin.

divided into zones called municipalities. Namibia has introduced a new system of decentralized government which divides the country into 13 regions. Kavango is one such region and people there are represented by regional councillors, one for each of nine constituencies. One of the councillors is appointed as the Regional Governor. The authority of regional governments is rather limited, although they will be expected to take more responsibility for regional affairs in the future. There are eight districts in Botswana, each headed by a District Commissioner as the representative of the central government. The Commissioner is in charge of the district administration, which is responsible for the provision of primary schooling, primary health care, community development and the maintenance of minor roads.

2
LANDSCAPES

The shape of a river

Near Menongue, the Cuebe River has cut down through layers of Kalahari sand to expose rocks formed between 2,500 and 1,800 million years ago.

A HOST OF FACTORS such as the relief of the land surface, geological structures and rainfall determine the way in which rivers flow. The nature of water flow and shape of continents also means that most rivers around the world carry their water down to the sea. But the Okavango stops in a delta in the middle of a semi-desert, and the delta is over a thousand kilometres from the sea, midway between the east and west coasts of southern Africa. Why should this river be so unusual? The following pages attempt to answer this question by providing a brief overview of the geological history of southern Africa. The story focuses on the three major features that dominate the foundations surrounding and underlying the river basin: the well-watered highland catchment in Angola, the vast expanse of Kalahari sands across which the river flows, and the set of natural walls that confine the Delta. The chapter also looks at the shape and relief of the river, potential mineral resources and the nature of soils in and around the river system.

Geological origins[1]

The origins of the oldest rocks in the Basin are difficult to explain, partly because they were formed so long ago. The shapes of the continents and oceans were then completely different from what they are now, and rocks have been eroded, moved and remoulded in more recent times. However, various volcanic and metamorphic processes between 2,500 and 1,800 million years ago formed all the granite, quartzite and gneiss rocks that make up part of the highland catchment in Angola **(Figure 3)**. That these rocks now stand as a highland is, however, a consequence of more recent events that lifted the edges of the African continent.

The ancient rocks were pushed into their current position by a series of movements of the Earth's plates between 700 and 550 million years ago. The shifts caused several landmasses to move towards each other and join to form what became the continent of Gondwana, and it was Gondwana's land surface that really provided the foundation or basement on which the Okavango river system now lies. This surface consisted of the old rocks formed much earlier but also a complex of so-called Damara Group rocks that were consolidated as the continents collided. These were originally sediments that had been deposited in rift valleys and oceans between the continents. The deposits were then forced upward as the continents pushed up against each other, the forces of compression heating and moulding the deposits into

mountains of dolomite, schist and sandstone. Most of the mountains have since eroded away, but remnants remain in eastern Angola and north-western Zambia, as the highlands in central Namibia and belt extending north-eastwards to south of the Delta, and as scattered outcrops in southern Kavango and western Ngamiland. The barrier of rocks over which the Popa Falls cascade is also Damara Group rocks.

The erosion of the Damara mountains continued over the next 350 million years, smoothing and carving Gondwana's landscape and producing new deposits of material eroded off the highlands. Climates fluctuated from dry to wet, or hot to cold. Wind was the main agent of deposition during dry periods, vast seas of sand dunes then being formed. Glaciers scoured the earth's surface during ice ages, and during very wet periods, rivers deposited sediments into massive lakes to form thick layers of mud and other sediments. Plant material in the lakes was later turned to coal, mud became shale while sand dunes were compressed into hard sandstone. Remnants of the sand dunes and lake deposits can now be seen in so-called Karoo rocks formed between 300 and 180 million years ago.

The belt of Karoo-age sandstone on the surface in central Namibia was perhaps formed from dunes deposited in an ancient rift valley. The belt extends as a broad strip below the surface into Ngamiland and underlies much of the Delta **(Figure 3)**. This orientation – from south-west to north-east – is the same as that of many faults in this wider area of central southern Africa. Some of the faults determine the shape of the Delta (see below), and follow a zone of weakness in the crust that may be an extension of the East African rift valley system that runs all the way from the Arabian peninsula south to Malawi, Zambia and Zimbabwe. The valley is now most prominent in East Africa and Malawi, while the arm that extends into Botswana and Namibia has probably never been activated sufficiently for deep valleys to be formed.

Gondwana was a huge expanse of land, but its life came to an end when it started breaking apart about 180 million years ago. The first ruptures caused the parting of what was to become Antarctica and southern Africa. More breaks followed about 132 million years ago when South America began drifting away from Africa, a process that continues today. Terrific volcanic explosions accompanied the breaks, lava forcing its way up through tears in the earth's crust and spewing out over tens of thousands of square kilometres. Relatively few of those volcanic rocks

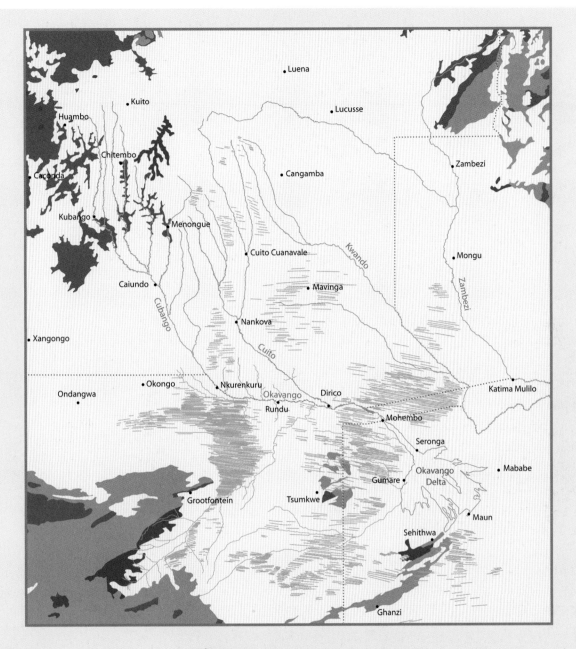

Kalahari Group
65 million years ago to the present

Karoo Group
300 - 180 million years ago

Damara Group
700 - 550 million years ago

Oldest rocks
2,500 - 1,800 million years ago

Dunes
2 million - 20,000 years ago

International boundary

Figure 3

Geological features formed during four major periods dominate the area in and around the Okavango Basin. For much of its length the river flows across Kalahari sands and other sediments laid down during the past 65 million years. Karoo rocks were mostly deposited between 300 and 180 million years ago, while Damara Group rocks formed when the continent of Gondwana was created between 700 and 550 million years ago. The oldest rocks developed between 2,500 and 1,800 million years ago. The map also shows the distribution of dunes moulded during previous arid periods. The most recent phase that was dry enough for the formation of dunes ended some 20,000 years ago. The orientation of the dunes reflects the direction of winds prevailing during those more arid periods. Consequently, most dunes lie to the west of the major rivers and Delta from where much of the dune sand was scoured by easterly winds.[2]

Popa Falls, where the river cascades down several metres before resuming its normal slow and leisurely flow. The rocks were formed from sediments deposited in rift valleys about 900 million years ago.

remain exposed on the surface in the area underlying the Okavango because most were covered by sediments laid down more recently.

Interestingly, extensions of the belt of faults that run south-west to north-east through Botswana and Namibia can be traced along the same axis into South America. The zone of weakness in the crust thus possibly first appeared in Gondwana when South America and Africa were joined. Around the Okavango Delta, two faults lie along the immediate south-eastern edge of the alluvial fan where they effectively form a wall that stops further spread of the Delta to the south-east **(Figure 4)**. The two faults, the Kunyere and Thamalakane faults, rise to the south-east and dip to the north-west. In most places the faults rise no more than five or ten metres on the surface. Another fault, the Gumare, separates the Panhandle from the

alluvial fan, but this dips from north-west to south-east. Two other perpendicular faults may have given rise to the relatively high ridges of Kalahari sand on either side of the Panhandle.

In a process and for reasons that are not clear, the margins of southern Africa apparently began to lift up after it and South America shifted apart, although some of the highlands may have risen above the landscape before Gondwana splintered and others may have been pushed up more recently. Whatever the circumstances, this left a rim of highlands surrounding a massive shallow basin in the middle of southern Africa. The rim stretches from central Angola southwards and then all the way round Africa to eastern Africa. A part of the depression is called the Kalahari Basin and it is into this bowl that the Okavango flows **(Figure 5)**. The bowl consists of two

The sharp edge at the bottom of the alluvial fan is formed by a rise in elevations along the Kunyere and Thamalakane faults. The fan can thus not grow any further to the south-east, but its sides are not confined and the remnants of much larger regions of flooding are visible as the greyish areas on either side of the present fan.

Legend:
1 – Tsodilo Hills
2 – Panhandle
3 – Gumare fault
4 – Old sand dunes
5 – Areas flooded previously
6 – Lake Ngami
7 – Kunyere fault
8 – Thamalakane fault
9 – Boteti River
10 – Mababe Depression
11 – Kwando River and Linyanti Swamps
12 – Selinda Spillway

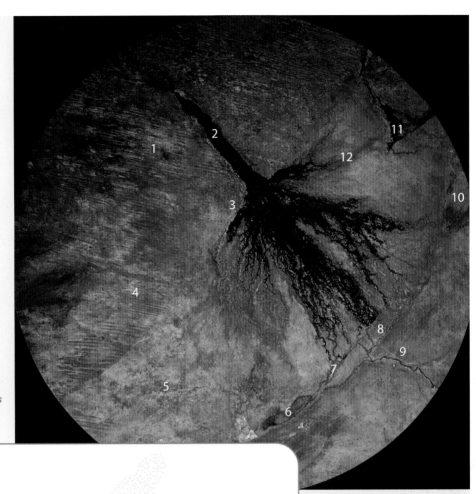

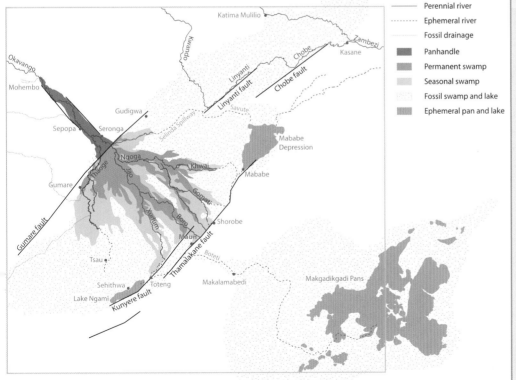

Figure 4

The south-eastern limits of the Delta are confined by the Kunyere and Thamalakane faults. Other faults that run along the same axis and also dip from east to west restrict the Kwando (forcing it to flow north into the Linyanti Swamps) and Chobe rivers. All these faults were formed in a zone of weakness that probably first formed as far back as 250 million years ago. Continuing movements of the faults cause small earthquakes so that frequent shudders and tremors are recorded around the Delta. The biggest recent tremor at Maun measured 6.7 on the Richter scale in 1952. The map also shows the extent of flooding during wetter periods and when the forerunner of the Zambezi used to flow south into Botswana.

35

sub-Basins: the southern Kalahari centred on Botswana and the Calondo sub-Basin in Angola. The southern sub-Basin may only be about 65 million years old while the Calondo was formed at least 180 million years ago.

The surface of the Kalahari Basin is now remarkably flat, even though it remains a depression with elevations dropping gradually from the margins towards the centre and lowest areas in the Makgadikgadi Pans in Botswana. Its flat surface is a consequence of the Basin being filled by sediments deposited over the past 65 million years. During most of the first 63 million years of its history sediments carried by rivers were laid down in huge lakes and deltas, and it is only during the past two million years that much of the Basin has dried up. Rivers much bigger than the Okavango have flowed into the Basin. For example, there is good evidence that the Zambezi ran here as recently as 50,000 years ago, before being captured by a river that had cut its way back from the east coast.[3] The Zambezi now carries about four times more water than the Okavango, and so imagine how

much water it, the Kwando and Okavango together brought into north-eastern Botswana when average rainfalls were perhaps double or more the amounts we receive now. These are the kinds of inflows that created lakes covering about 120,000 square kilometres around the Delta and Makgadikgadi Pans. That would be about ten times bigger than the present Delta **(Figure 4)**.

How old is the river? This is a difficult question because climates have changed so much. A better approach is to ask the age of the river as we know it, and to ask if the river existed in some other form long ago. Starting with the second aspect, rivers must have started to flow into the Kalahari Basin soon after it formed and it seems possible that one of those rivers evolved into the Okavango. Theories have even been developed to suggest that a quite different Okavango cut across the Kalahari to flow all the way into what is now the Orange or the Limpopo River,[4] but more research is needed to establish whether any large river flowed all that way.

Looking at the river as it is now, the tributaries of the Cubango, Cutato, Cuchi and Cutato rivers have a clear trellis pattern because most join the main rivers at right-angles. These angles and the almost perfectly parallel courses of the four rivers suggest that they are very young, perhaps less than several million years old. However, it is also obvious that these and other parts of the river system would have been altered in accordance with changes in climate. During very wet periods much bigger areas were flooded in the Delta and more aggressive flows would have caused rivers to cut new courses. Some of these would have been obliterated during dry cycles when the rivers dried up and much of the area was covered in sand dunes. And then new channels and valleys would have opened up when heavy rains fell in the next wet phase. The Delta is, of course, built of layers of sediment, and its surface now lies between 100 and 270 metres above a basement of rock. How much of the sediment above the bedrock was laid down within the Delta and how much was deposited by wind during drier times or quite different river, lake or delta systems is not known.

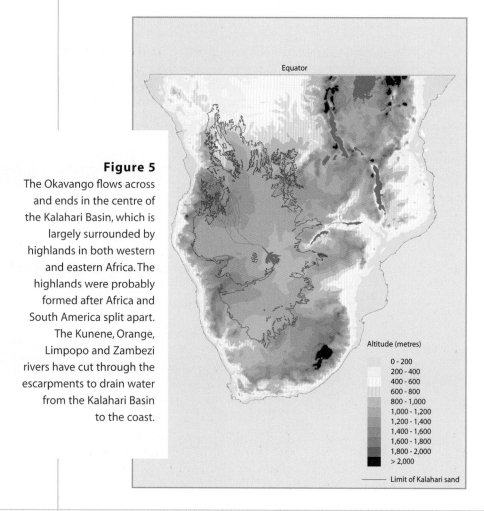

Figure 5
The Okavango flows across and ends in the centre of the Kalahari Basin, which is largely surrounded by highlands in both western and eastern Africa. The highlands were probably formed after Africa and South America split apart. The Kunene, Orange, Limpopo and Zambezi rivers have cut through the escarpments to drain water from the Kalahari Basin to the coast.

Equator

Altitude (metres)

0 - 200
200 - 400
400 - 600
600 - 800
800 - 1,000
1,000 - 1,200
1,200 - 1,400
1,400 - 1,600
1,600 - 1,800
1,800 - 2,000
> 2,000

——— Limit of Kalahari sand

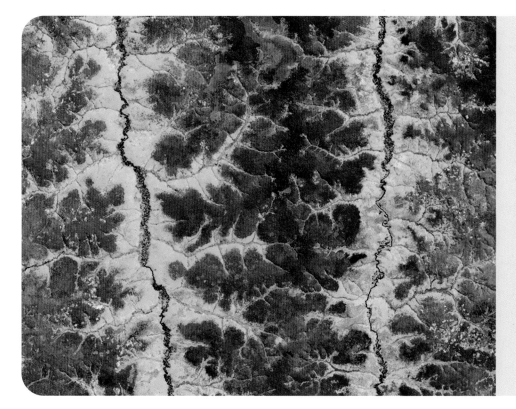

Rivers in the north-west of the catchment have developed recently – perhaps during the last few million years – because their trellis-like pattern is characteristic of recently established drainages. The rivers still drain areas of Kalahari sand deposits in some areas while in others the rivers have cut through the sands and now flow off basement rocks of granite, quartzite and gneiss.

Diamonds and other riches

Angola, Namibia and Botswana all earn a high proportion of their income from mineral resources, especially diamonds, gold, coal and oil. However, none of this revenue comes from the Basin because there is not a single mine anywhere near the river system. This is mainly a consequence of the thick mantle of Kalahari deposits. Finding minerals deep beneath the deposits is one major challenge; others are to overcome technical and financial constraints to reach the minerals. However, this has not stopped many people from speculating that riches are to be found, especially diamonds in Angola. With the opening up of southern Angola many prospectors are now scouring the area for new deposits. Speculation is also fuelled by the presence of diamond diggings near Mavinga, 150 kilometres east of Cuito Cuanavale. These diamonds are probably associated with basement rock underlying the Kwando River drainage that is old enough to contain economic kimberlites. By contrast, basement rocks to the west of the Cuito River appear too young to hold much potential for diamondiferous kimberlites.

Further south in Namibia, prospecting is underway in the Kavango part of the Basin, where four kimberlites have been found near Sikeretti and across the border at Nxaunxau in Ngamiland. Some micro-diamonds and minerals associated with diamonds have been found in Kavango, suggesting that economic diamonds might be found. However, more exploration is needed before such a possibility is shown to be valid or not. Other than diamonds, the only other deposits that may be of significance are coal, oil and gas. Deposits of these may be found in Karoo-age rocks, but again they lie deep below the surface and little exploratory work has been done to determine if any useful resources are present.

The relief of the Okavango

The whole river system gradually winds its way across the Kalahari Basin from the highest elevations of between 1,700 and 1,800 metres on the Basin's rim to the bottom of the Delta at 940 metres above sea level **(Figure 6)**. The north-western catchment and highest ground consists of ancient basement rocks covered by patches of Kalahari sand, while the north-eastern reaches of the catchment comprise only Kalahari sand. These two northerly catchment areas lie either side of a giant amphitheatre some 200 kilometres in diameter. This is the most southerly catchment of the Cuanza River, which flows north and then west to its estuary on the Atlantic coast 60 kilometres south of Luanda. The Cuanza flows much more rapidly than any of the Okavango rivers because it drops so much (about 1,500 metres) over a relatively short distance. It is thus a more 'aggressive' river, cutting back and eroding away the ground in its catchment. The walls of the amphitheatre drop rather steeply by about 200 metres into the Cuanza catchment, unlike the much more gentle slopes around the headwaters of Okavango rivers to the south of the watershed.

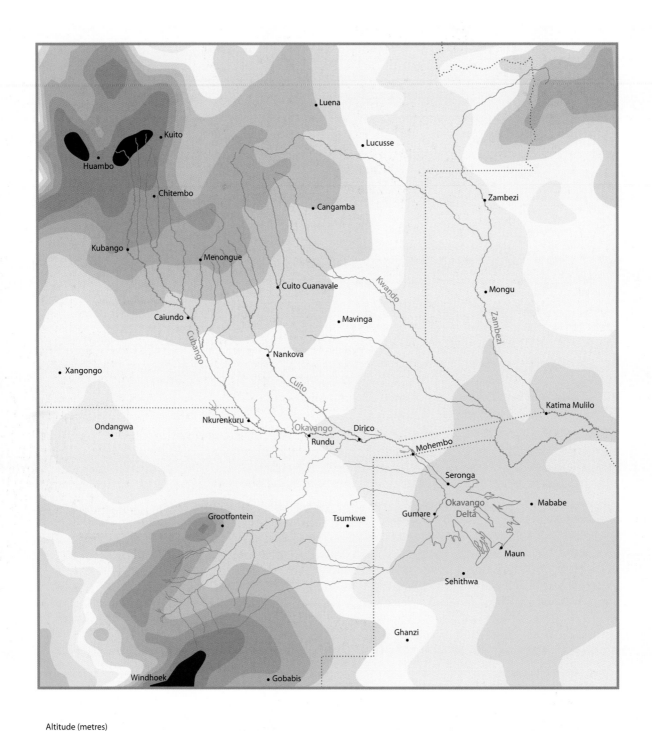

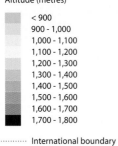

- < 900
- 900 - 1,000
- 1,000 - 1,100
- 1,100 - 1,200
- 1,200 - 1,300
- 1,300 - 1,400
- 1,400 - 1,500
- 1,500 - 1,600
- 1,600 - 1,700
- 1,700 - 1,800

········· International boundary

Figure 6

The Okavango starts its flow southwards from about 1,700 metres above sea level (asl) and ends at about 940 metres asl, at the base of the Kunyere and Thamalakane faults on the south-eastern edge of the Delta. The Cuito headwaters lie at just over 1,500 metres asl, about half a kilometre higher than its confluence with the Okavango at just over 1,000 metres asl.

A typical landscape of gentle rolling hills separated by broad shallow valleys in the Angolan highlands in the north-western catchment. The area is high only in relation to the much lower southern parts of the river Basin. The main valley in the centre is that of the Cutato River, while the tributary in the foreground is characteristic of the hundreds of tributaries that give the rivers in this area a trellis-like drainage pattern.

A birds-eye view of the Basin stretching away from the Delta in the foreground to the highest areas in the Angolan catchment. The Omatako flows out of higher ground south-west of Grootfontein. Note the clearly defined amphitheatre shape between the Cubango and Cuito. This depression forms the headwaters of the Cuanza River which flows north and then west to the Atlantic.

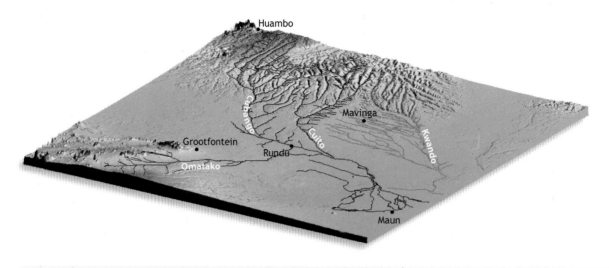

Figure 7

All the Okavango's rivers or tributaries have extremely gentle flows over most of their lengths. The steepest gradients and fastest flows are in the headwaters. The graphs show the altitudes of the Cuito and Cubango/ Okavango rivers in relation to the distance from their source.

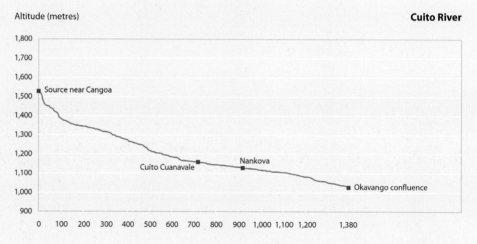

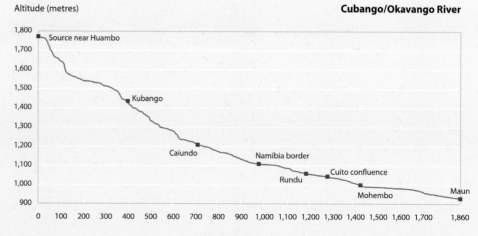

Gradients across the river system are steepest in the north-western catchment and shallowest in the Delta **(Figure 7)**. Rivers in the north-west thus drop by about 300 metres over distances of 300 kilometres. Numerically, this is a gradient of approximately 1:1,000, three to five times steeper than slopes of 1:5,000 in the Panhandle and 1:3,300 in the alluvial fan of the Delta. In fact, elevations drop only 61 metres over 250 kilometres, the distance from the top of the Panhandle to the Thamalakane River at Maun. This gentle slope is one reason why the river's water takes about four months to reach the south-eastern edge of the Delta (see page 85).

The densest network of tributaries is in the north-west where the countryside is hilliest, the bedrock is exposed and the mantle of Kalahari sand is thin. Elsewhere, the landscape of thick sand is much flatter and active drainage lines are spaced far apart. Some tributaries also follow interesting courses. For example those joining the Cubango, Cutato, Cuchi and Cacuchi rivers flow into the rivers at roughly perpendicular angles. The valleys of the Cutato and Cuchi are generally symmetrical so that tributaries from the east and west are similar in length. However, those of the Cubango and Cacuchi are shaped unevenly with the result that western tributaries are considerably longer than the ones from the east. Those patterns of symmetry and asymmetry hold true along the whole lengths of the four river valleys. Many of the tributaries to the Cuanavale run from southeast to northwest along old fossilized interdune valleys, which means that the direction of flow changes abruptly once water reaches the south-flowing main river.

Soils

In one form or another, soils are important to all life in the Okavango Basin. They provide the medium from which plants obtain water and nutrients, and properties of the soils determine what plant species are present and thus the value and diversity of vegetation communities. Properties of soils vary in terms of their depth, structure and chemical composition, and these affect how much water soils retain, the depth to which roots extend, and what nutrients are available. The physical structure of plant communities is also influenced by soils. A plant species may be stunted in one area of shallow or sterile soil but it will grow tall in deep soils rich in

Rivers in the northwestern catchment cascade over rapids or small waterfalls in many places. The straight lines that break the fall of water along the Cubango are probably layers in a stratified rock formation (left)*, while the small waterfall on the Cutato* (right) *was once identified as a potential site for a hydroelectric dam during the 1960s.*

nutrients elsewhere. All these effects are particularly relevant to crop cultivation, and the generally poor quality of soils in the Basin (see below) has major impacts on the types of crops grown and their yields (see page 141).

Another significant effect of soils in the Basin is on the quality of water. Compared to most other rivers, the waters of the Okavango contain exceptionally small amounts of mud and dissolved chemicals or minerals (see page 92). The main reason for the clarity and purity is that most water filters out of sandy soils made up largely of quartz grains. These do not easily dissolve or break-up to release soluble chemicals or tiny particles that would otherwise be washed into the river as minerals and mud. The sands also serve to moderate the flow of water since most rainwater sinks into the ground rather than running off the surface and into the tributaries of the major

rivers. Flows are thus much more even than those along rivers that drain rocky areas. Within the catchment the effects of sand in providing clean and steady flows are more pronounced in the sandiest areas, especially in the Cuito sub-Basin (see page 83). Flows off basement rocks in the hillier Cubango sub-Basin are more variable and most of the nutrients and sediments that find their way to the Delta probably come from this western area.

The map of soils **(Figure 8)** provides a rough perspective on how soils vary across the Basin. Its roughness is due to the absence of better information for Angola as well as the scale of mapping. Every farmer knows how much soils vary – even within the same field – and it is simply impossible at the kind of scale used here to reflect the patchiness of soils. The map thus attempts to show what types of soil dominate in different areas.

Thick layers of Kalahari sands have been cut away and exposed by this meander on the Cuito River 140 kilometres north of Cuito Cuanavale.

The fine to medium arenosol sands that characterize so much of the Basin are more generally called Kalahari sands. The sands often extend to a depth of at least one metre. Sand grains usually make up more than 70% of the body of the soil and less than 10% consists of clay and silt. There are few nutrients (especially nitrogen, potassium and phosphorous) in the sand and the porous structure means that there is little run-off or water erosion. Water drains through the body of soil rapidly, leaving little moisture at depths to which most plant roots can reach.

The fluvisols shown in **Figure 8** are limited to areas immediately along the major rivers, but fluvisol soils are also found along the many smaller tributaries. Fluvisols were deposited by high water flows on floodplains and are usually characterized elsewhere in the world by a rich organic and nutrient content. However, this is probably only true for fluvisols in the Delta where nutrients have progressively accumulated over long periods. The sediments usually consist of a mix of silt, clay and fine sands.

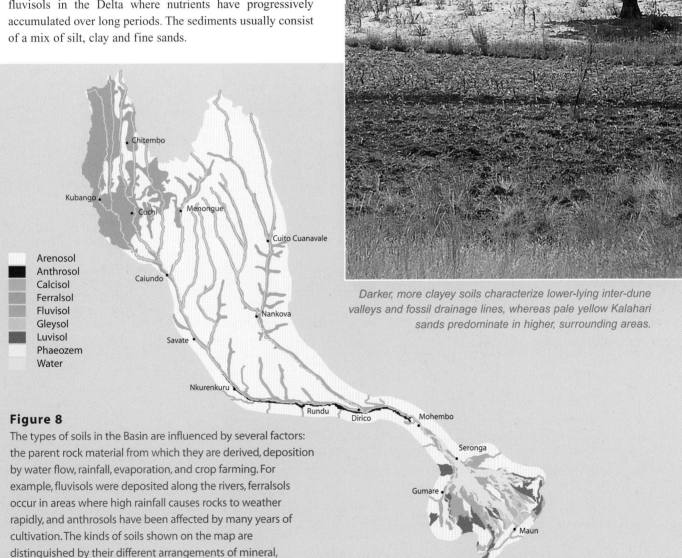

Darker, more clayey soils characterize lower-lying inter-dune valleys and fossil drainage lines, whereas pale yellow Kalahari sands predominate in higher, surrounding areas.

Arenosol
Anthrosol
Calcisol
Ferralsol
Fluvisol
Gleysol
Luvisol
Phaeozem
Water

Figure 8

The types of soils in the Basin are influenced by several factors: the parent rock material from which they are derived, deposition by water flow, rainfall, evaporation, and crop farming. For example, fluvisols were deposited along the rivers, ferralsols occur in areas where high rainfall causes rocks to weather rapidly, and anthrosols have been affected by many years of cultivation. The kinds of soils shown on the map are distinguished by their different arrangements of mineral, organic, water and air components within the soil body.[5]

A zone of anthrosols is shown on the southern bank of the river in Kavango. These are soils modified by repeated ploughing and crop production. Smaller areas of anthrosols farmed over long periods in Angola and around the Delta have not been mapped. These soils usually consist of a layer of arenosols overlying deeper deposits of fluvisol sediments, and the layers have since been mixed by ploughing. Anthrosols generally have a low nutrient content. Concerns are often raised about soil erosion as a result of the extensive clearing of land on the southern bank in Kavango. However, this potential problem, and possible increased levels of sediments in the river, requires more investigation.

Calcisols occur along fossil drainage lines in Kavango and adjacent areas in southern Angola. Layers of calcium carbonate salts lying at some depth below the surface characterize these soils, which consist mostly of fine sand and smaller proportions of clay and silt. The calcium carbonate sometimes forms blocks of calcrete. The soils are used for crops because they are potentially quite fertile and retain water to a much greater degree than arenosols.

Ferralsols are widely distributed in the northwestern upper catchment where they have developed as a result of weathering of basement rocks **(see Figure 3)**. The soils are noted for the dominance of kaolinite clays. However, their low nutrient reserves are easily and rapidly exhausted by crop production. Ferralsols are often very deep, permeable and have a stable soil structure, three qualities that make them resistant to water erosion.

Three soils in the Delta directly or indirectly owe their formation to flooding and the presence of decomposed plant material. Phaeozems are found only in the outer reaches of the Delta area where there is infrequent flooding. An accumulation of organic matter on the surface is characteristic of phaeozem soils, which are porous and well-aerated. They are also relatively rich in nutrients and have good agricultural potential. Luvisols are also present around the edges of the Delta, and these are potentially the most fertile soils as a result of deep accumulations of clay and organic material. They, too, are porous and usually retain high levels of moisture. The formation of gleysols is partly due to water logging at shallow depths for some or all of the year. Prolonged water saturation in the presence of organic matter results in the formation of grey, olive or blue-coloured layers beneath the surface.

From this account it should be clear that the greatest area of the Basin consists of soils poorly suited to

agriculture, and the only small areas with fertile soils are in the Delta. The concept of soil quality is a relative one, however. For example, people in Kavango often see any soil that contains some moisture and nutrients as being 'a good soil' because so many areas are unsuitable for crops. But Angolan farmers have better soils to choose from and would probably reject what would be the best soils available in Kavango. There are several implications of such generally poor soils. The first is that small-scale farmers will usually not achieve good yields, especially if they do not apply manure, compost or fertilizers. A second consequence is that large-scale, commercial and irrigated crop

Kalahari sands are poorly suited to crop production because they hold few nutrients and little water. These constraints can be overcome by adding fertilizers, which are relatively expensive and must be applied carefully, and water, in this case through centre-pivot irrigation at Shadikongoro. Maize, cotton and wheat are the main crops grown here.

production will normally require large applications of fertilizers. Thirdly, the application of fertilizers will require careful management to ensure that the correct minerals or nutrients are applied at appropriate times and in adequate amounts. Finally, there is a danger that fertilizers will find their way into the Okavango system, particularly in places where run-off or seepage easily finds its way into nearby rivers.

Key points

■ Tectonic and metamorphic processes between 2,500 and 1,800 million years ago (mya) formed the granite, quartzite and gneiss rocks in the north-west catchment in Angola.

■ The foundation on which much of the river system lies was produced between 700 to 550 mya when the continent of Gondwana was formed.

■ Gondwana started to break apart 180 mya, while South America and Africa parted ways 132 mya.

■ The break-up of Gondwana was followed by the margins of southern Africa being lifted to produce a rim of highlands surrounding a massive shallow basin. Part of this is the Kalahari Basin, which started to fill with sediments 65 mya.

■ As recently as 50,000 years ago, much larger flows of water into the Delta and surrounding areas were at times carried by the Okavango, Kwando, the Zambezi and other rivers.

■ There are no minerals of economic importance now known in the Basin.

■ The Okavango's rivers flow from the highest elevations of between 1,700 and 1,800 metres to the bottom of the Delta at 940 metres above sea level. Gradients generally become gentler along the course of the river.

■ The densest network of tributaries is in the north-west where it is hilliest, the bedrock is exposed and the mantle of Kalahari sand is thin. Elsewhere, the landscape of thick sand is flatter and active drainage lines are far apart.

■ The predominance of sand in the catchment results in the river water being very clean with low contents of minerals and mud. The sand also gives the river a more even flow than would be the case in a rocky catchment.

■ Most soils in the Basin are not good for crop growth as result of low nutrient levels and poor water retention. Only certain areas in the Delta have good quality soils.

3

THE PAST

Trying times

Over 4,000 individual paintings have been found at Tsodilo Hills, 50 kilometres to the west of the Panhandle. Excavations indicate that Tsodilo has been occupied continuously over the past 50,000 to 40,000 years, first by hunter-gatherers and then by livestock and crop farmers from about 1,500 years ago.[1]

THE ENGLISH EXPLORER and missionary David Livingstone trekked for months across the Kalahari to reach Lake Ngami in 1849, and Alexandre Serpa Pinto, a Portuguese explorer and surveyor, battled for months to reach the headwaters of the river system in 1877. Nowadays, anyone from any part of the Earth can reach the heart of the Delta in one or two days. The journey is comfortable, water is on tap everywhere, and the traveller is protected from disease. We can also see any piece of the globe in satellite pictures, and dozens of documentary films bring home the nature and character of places far away.

Nothing is remote, and little is beyond easy reach. All this is possible because of new technology: aeroplanes, cars, good roads, film and satellites, utilities most of us take for granted. We also readily accept the fact that many people are now attracted to the Okavango. But this, too, is new. Until recently the whole Okavango River system was isolated: unknown to most people in the world and also to most citizens of Angola, Namibia and Botswana. Only certain people made the trip: folk pushed away from their homes in other parts of southern Africa, explorers such as Serpa Pinto and Livingstone, and traders in search of slaves and ivory. Incidentally, the capital of Kuando Kubango – Menongue – was named Villa Serpa Pinto until recently.

Many books could be written about the history of the Okavango Basin. The few pages here cover aspects we believe have a bearing on the Basin as it is today. Thus, the area was always sparsely populated, partly for reasons of disease, warfare and slavery. Leadership systems were generally weak, and most inhabitants are descended from groups that moved into the Basin quite recently. Outsiders either ignored or neglected the area, much of which was called the *as terra do fim do Mundo* – the place at the end of the earth. Generations of people were subjected to extreme inhumanity, and it is only in recent decades that law and order started to prevail in certain places. History, in summary, has not treated people in the Basin kindly.

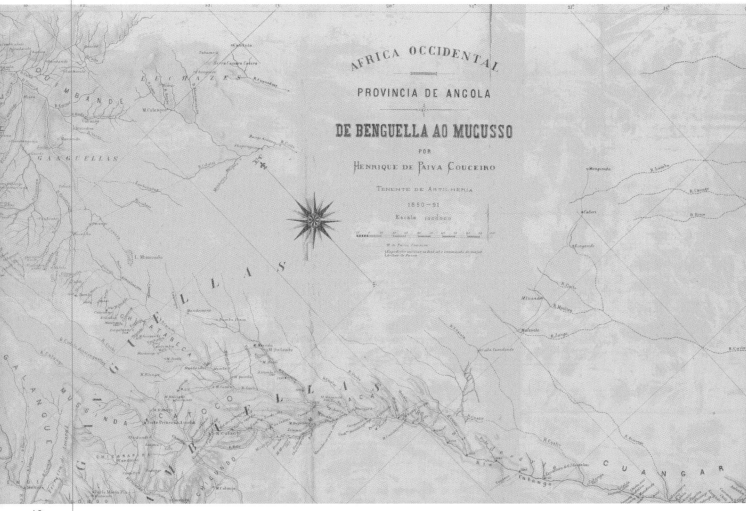

Images of life and colonial exploration in the Basin a century ago are provided by old maps, such as this one compiled (opposite, bottom) in 1890–1891, and photographs taken during the 1903 Kunene-Sambesi Expedition of the Kolonial Wirtschaftliches Komitee.[2] The bundles of roots are reported to be those of Landolphia, from which rubber was extracted and exported to the Angolan coast (right), while the decorated hut (centre) was photographed at Longa. One of the three people in the picture at the bottom was the king of the Kwangali people who lived along the middle reaches of the Cubango/Okavango.

The earliest times

That the Okavango was remote and neglected for much of history is true, but some people inhabited the Basin for hundreds of thousands of years. The earliest firm indication of human life comes in the form of stone tools found at several places. These all date from the Early and Middle Stone Ages and were produced between at least 200,000 up to 35,000 years ago **(Figure 9)**. That all Late Stone Age sites from between 35,000 and 2,000 years ago are in Ngamiland is a reflection of the more extensive archaeological research that has taken place there than in Kavango and the Angolan provinces. There is, indeed, no reason to suppose that any one area of the Basin was occupied more intensely than any other, and many more sites will be found as archaeologists explore further. Climatic conditions during the past were often quite different from those of today (see page 67). Patterns of settlement changed, people being more widely distributed during wetter periods and then more concentrated near river water in arid phases.

Livelihoods during that long history were based on hunting, fishing and gathering, and most researchers agree that people living during the more recent Late Stone Age would have been so-called Khoesan people. Some Khoesan remained as hunter-gatherers and the ancestors of modern San people, but others switched to livestock farming. Farming could have started here as long as 2,000 years ago after Bantu farmers arrived in southern Africa from east and west Africa. Most sites

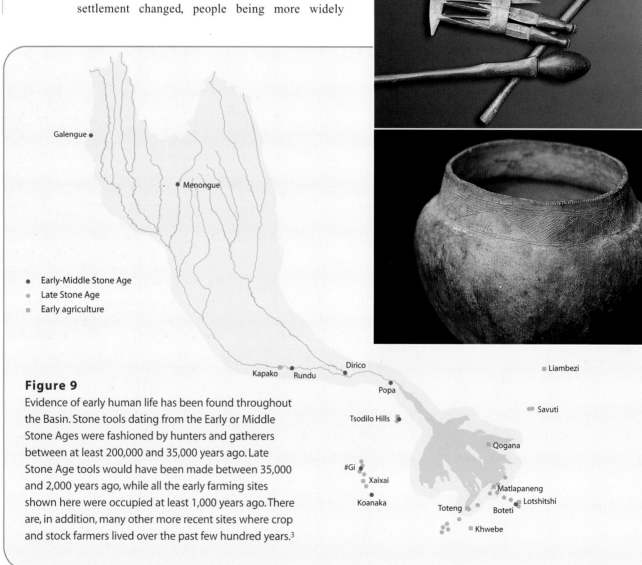

Figure 9

Evidence of early human life has been found throughout the Basin. Stone tools dating from the Early or Middle Stone Ages were fashioned by hunters and gatherers between at least 200,000 and 35,000 years ago. Late Stone Age tools would have been made between 35,000 and 2,000 years ago, while all the early farming sites shown here were occupied at least 1,000 years ago. There are, in addition, many other more recent sites where crop and stock farmers lived over the past few hundred years.[3]

- ● Early-Middle Stone Age
- ● Late Stone Age
- ■ Early agriculture

Galengue

Menongue

Kapako Rundu Dirico

Popa

Liambezi

Savuti

Tsodilo Hills

Qogana

#Gi

Xaixai

Matlapaneng

Lotshitshi

Koanaka

Toteng Boteti

Khwebe

showing evidence of farming in **Figure 9** date from between 1,500 and 1,000 years ago. The remains of livestock, crops and pots used to store grain at these sites are often accompanied by evidence of iron working, this too being an innovation brought south by Bantu immigrants. Glass beads, copper and cowry shells indicate that people in the Basin then had widespread trading contacts across much of southern Africa. More recently during the 1700s and 1800s people in the Angolan highlands were famous as traders of wax, rubber and honey, selling or exchanging these goods on the coast.

Artifacts offer glimpses of lifestyles and values from the past: clay pots were used for grain storage by the earliest crop farmers (opposite bottom), *evidence of widespread trading comes from the presence in the Basin of marine cowry shells* (right below), *while bows and arrows* (right) *and knives and axes* (opposite top) *emphasize the importance of hunting long ago.*

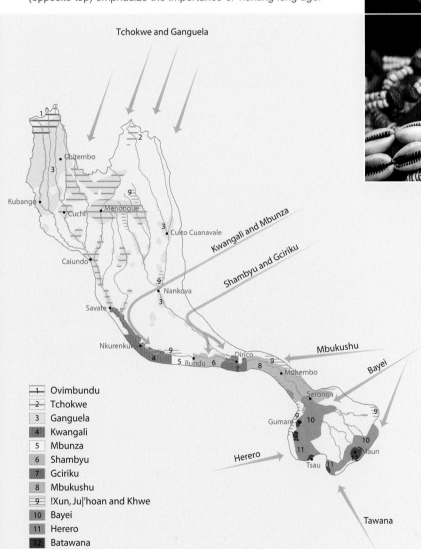

1 Ovimbundu
2 Tchokwe
3 Ganguela
4 Kwangali
5 Mbunza
6 Shambyu
7 Gciriku
8 Mbukushu
9 !Xun, Ju|'hoan and Khwe
10 Bayei
11 Herero
12 Batawana

Figure 10

Approximate and broad distributions of dominant language groups in the Basin, the arrows indicating the directions from which their ancestors probably came. Accounts of most movements have been passed down as oral traditions from generation to generation. The legends can be interpreted in various ways and opinions often differ on when the movements occurred. For example, there are claims that no one lived along the Okavango before the immigrations of clans that gave rise to the Kwangali, Mbunza, Shambyu and Gciriku, but others suggest that the river valley was already inhabited by Bayei or Tjaube and Khwe people. In fact, it is clear the river was home to people for tens and perhaps hundreds of thousands of years, but it remains an open question as to who they were.[4]

Populations in and around the Basin were small over all these tens of thousands of years, and it was only during the last 100 years ago that populations really expanded (see page 128). Three factors limited the number of people. First, diseases such as malaria and sleeping sickness were extremely prevalent, and child mortality rates were high because children were often affected. Second, numbers were kept in check by frequent raids to steal cattle, and slaves and women to boost the labour force and populations of the raiders. Most raids came from the bigger kingdoms, such as those of the Ovimbundu, Lunda, Tchokwe in central and northern Angola, the Kwanyama in central northern Namibia and Kolololo from Lesotho. Tribes in the Basin were often helpless because they were small and lacked strong leadership. Finally and most importantly, areas to the north and east were more attractive as places to live because they offered higher rainfall and better soils on which to grow crops.

People on the move

Apart from San people, most inhabitants of the Basin belong to groups that moved here during the past few hundred years **(Figure 10)**. What is more, most groups came to live here because they were under pressure where they lived originally. For example, most Herero people are descended from those who fled German troops in Namibia during the 1904–1907 Nama-Herero war against German forces. The majority of people living in Kavango are descended from Angolans that moved south over many generations (see page 129), first to escape tribal raids and disease and then slave traders and the hardships of Portuguese rule. More recent emigrations have been to flee civil strife after Angola's 1975 independence and to benefit from better services and economic opportunities in Kavango.

Both the Ganguela and Tchokwe people are thought to have arrived in the upper Basin area from further north in central Africa, perhaps between the 1300s and 1600s. The Tchokwe later moved further south from eastern Angola to escape slave raids. Accounts passed down over the years relate how the Kwangali, Mbunza, Shambyu and Gciriku tribes all had their origins along the upper reaches of the Zambezi River. Small groups or clans left, moving first south and west to the

Fishing has supported livelihoods in the Basin for many thousands of years. Cowry shells were often used to adorn head dresses (bottom left).

Kwando River. One clan then travelled west to settle along the Cubango River in Angola, but was forced to leave by Imbangala people. They settled in western Kavango, but a disagreement between their leaders led to the clan dividing into two groups that were to become the tribes now known as the Kwangali and Mbunza. A different clan from the upper Zambezi moved down the Cuito to eastern Kavango and, again, a disagreement led to a division that gave rise to the Shambyu and Gciriku tribes.

Oral traditions also suggest that an expanding Lozi empire pushed both the Mbukushu and Bayei out of what is now Caprivi. Ngombela, the Lozi king, is said to have overcome the Bayei and Mbukushu after a series of attacks in about 1750. The Mbukushu lived along the Kwando River and then moved to the present Mukwe area and partly downstream along the Panhandle. Later movements of more Mbukushu to the Delta occurred in response to raids to gather slaves for Angola and, as recently as the 1970s, to the civil war in Angola. Their base remained at Mukwe, however, because Mbukushu chiefs lived on the nearby island of Thipanana up until 1900. The chiefs were famous rainmakers who were consulted by people from far and wide, and the island became a centre of trade between the east and west coasts of southern Africa. Payments of black cows and oxen, ivory and young women to the rainmaker provided the Mbukushu people with considerable wealth.

The first Batswana clan moved from near Shoshong in southern Botswana to the Khwebe Hills 25 kilometres from Lake Ngami. This was in the late 1700s or early 1800s, and it was caused by a dispute, between their leader (called Tawana) and his brother, on who would succeed as chief of the larger Tswana tribe. Although San people have probably lived here for hundreds of generations, they, too, have been dispossessed and pushed from their settlements to less favoured places. This is one reason why the San population is so small, scattered and marginalized. The most recent examples of such movements are the resettlement of San people from Angola and Kavango to South African military bases in Namibia south of Kavango during the 1970s, and the exodus of Khwe people to Botswana in 1999 following unrest in Caprivi.

Wholesale slavery

In the 1400s Portugal began venturing down the African coast, successive ships pushing and exploring further and further south. The first ship to reach Angola was under the command of Diogo Cão who erected a cross in 1483 south of what was to become the port of Benguela. A major purpose of the expeditions was to search for gold, but they found another more abundant commodity: slaves. For Angola, this marked the start of two periods of Portuguese influence. The first was essentially a commercial phase lasting from the early 1500s until the late 1800s, while the second was the colonial phase that ended with independence for Angola in 1975. Commercial activity centered on slaves and an estimated four million people were shipped out of Angola. About half the slaves were sent to Brazil, initially to work on Portuguese plantations, while another third were sold in the Caribbean. Yet others were sold at slave markets in West Africa, often to pay for gold to be carried home to Lisbon. The Portuguese slave traders operated as middlemen, buying slaves along the coast and then shipping off their human cargo for sale elsewhere. Much of the buying was at Luanda and Benguela, and Luanda was once called the slave capital of the world. The slaves were bought from Angolan traders who ventured far inland to obtain them for sale along the coast. Buying trips ventured as far south as the Delta in Botswana. It's possible that millions of people died en route to the slave shops on the coast. Slave trading also became rife within Angola, slaves being bought and sold to plantation growers in the central highlands and north of the country.

Slavery, in one form or another, had been going on within the continent for perhaps hundreds or thousands of years before the Portuguese started to export millions of slaves. To the east there was another slave trading power, that of Arab and Swahili merchants who travelled up and down the eastern coast of Africa. Most of their buying trips were to places closer to the coast, but Mbukushu leaders sold their own people, often as whole villages, as slaves to the Arab trade up until 1912.[5]

Chained slaves, ready to be marched off to a distant slave market.

Chiefs had a great many wives, many of whom might have been taken during raids of neighbouring tribes.

The Portuguese fort at Cuangar in about 1912; built to enable Portugal to establish control over the most remote parts of its new colony.

Portugal formally stopped the slave trade in Angola in 1858, but that didn't bring the practice to an end. Informal slave trading for labour on plantations within the country continued for several decades, and forced labour was only abolished by law in 1962. The effect of all of this is that Angolan society was consumed by the indignities of wholesale slavery for three to four hundred years, perhaps 15 generations! Little wonder that more recent periods of history have seen such disrespect for human life. The Portuguese did not introduce slavery but the scale and nature of slavery during those four hundred years was different. Many more people were taken and they were exported for the first time. The trade also served to enrich a handful of people: the Portuguese and Angolan traders and local chiefs who were rewarded with such payments as firearms, alcohol and clothes.

Colonizers

During the mid-1800s European powers came under increasing pressure to occupy more formally and effectively the areas they claimed, and they had to reach beyond the coast if they were to maintain a grip on their territories. Growing condemnation of slavery also stimulated a search for other resources. It was these kinds of motives that encouraged explorations into the interior of Africa, such as those that led David Livingstone to Lake Ngami in 1849, Alexandre Serpa Pinto to the headwaters of the river system in 1877, and Charles John Andersson to be the first European to see the Okavango River in 1859. The expeditions made the Basin known to the outside world for the first time.

The borders of Angola, Namibia and Botswana owe their origins to the Berlin Conference in 1884 and several treaties signed during the 1880s and 1890s between Portugal, Britain and Germany. This was the period when Africa was sliced up to give European powers their colonies and protectorates. Colonial administrators began to be posted inland, often to places where police stations, forts and labour recruiting centres were built. For example, the establishment of a police station in 1910 at Nkurenkuru provided the Germans with their first permanent presence in Kavango. Missionaries followed, with mission stations being founded at Nyangana in 1910, Andara in 1913, Nkurenkuru in 1926, Tondoro in 1927, Bunya in 1929 and Shambyu in 1930, for example. It was these missions that first introduced formal schooling and health services to Kavango.

Colonial control of Kavango shifted to South Africa in 1920 when it was given a mandate to administer the then South West Africa Protectorate, and for the next 70 years Kavango was really managed as a reserve for the Kavango people. The first superintendent of 'native affairs' was appointed in 1922, and in 1937 Kavango was formally declared as a tribal area, the 'Okavango Native Reserve'. The administrative centre of Kavango moved from Nkurenkuru to Rundu in 1936, which had been established as a recruiting centre to supply labour to white farms south of Kavango. Other than labour, Kavango had little to offer Namibia during all those colonial years, and development accordingly came slowly. Schools, health facilities, roads and other infrastructure were built here and there, but for government administrators Kavango was always a rather forsaken and remote part of Deutsch Südwes Afrika and later South West Africa.

On the other side of the Okavango, the Portuguese began asserting their territory by building forts at Cuangar, Dirico and Mucusso from 1909 onwards. Most early Portuguese administrators were *degrados*, convicts from Portugal, often guilty of serious crimes. These were the people expected to guide the development of the colony, but their behaviour frequently set bad examples for the people they were supposed to administer. Such influences, harsh racial discrimination, taxation and forced labour did little to endear Portugal to the Angolans or to develop a civil society. Other Portuguese began immigrating to Angola, often to establish farms and plantations to produce exports of coffee, sisal, cotton and rubber, for example. The government actively encouraged settlement in its colony from the early 1900s onwards.

For example, 55,000 Portuguese were brought to Angola as recently as between 1955 and 1960. Angola was correctly seen to be rich in resources, and Portugal's economic interests were reinforced by the discovery of diamonds in the 1920s and oil in the 1950s. Other resources were found or developed, such as iron, coffee and fish exports. However, the enormous increase in production that followed the arrival of immigrants and exploitation of resources all occurred to the north of the Okavango Basin: oil in Cabinda, diamonds in the north-east, farming and coffee plantations in the central highlands. The Basin area of Angola thus remained undeveloped and remote. A few missionaries ventured south, and a handful of schools, clinics, roads and farms were developed. Even though the railway line to Menongue was named the 'door to the wilderness', the area was still known as the *as terra do fim do Mundo*.

'We have no interest in the country to the north of the Molopo except as a road to the interior. We might therefore confine ourselves for the present to preventing that part of the protectorate being occupied by either filibusters or foreign powers, doing as little in the way of administration or settlement as possible.' That is how the High Commissioner of Britain summed up British interests shortly after it had gained Botswana as the Bechuanaland Protectorate in 1885.[6] The foreign powers referred particularly to the Germans to the west in Namibia and the Boer Republic in the Transvaal. Britain had no wish for either to expand their influence in southern Africa.

Very little development came to Botswana over the next 70 years. Administration of much of the land was left to traditional chiefs. Almost the only interest anyone outside Ngamiland had in the Okavango was as a source of water for grandiose schemes to irrigate huge areas in the Kalahari. Development in that area was also limited by the presence of sleeping sickness, the disease transmitted by tsetse flies (see page 123). The Moremi Game Reserve was proclaimed in 1963. This was shortly after Britain began to realize that political and economic independence had to come to Botswana. The capital of Gaborone was quickly built since the country had previously been administered from Mafikeng in South Africa, and Botswana became independent in 1966.

Recent dreams and nightmares

Recent years have seen Botswana achieve fame as a peaceful, prosperous and rapidly developing country: an African dream. The same years have seen Angola's reputation develop for prolonged civil war, disregard for human life, corruption and economic ruin: an international nightmare.

Angola became independent in 1975. Much of the country's expertise left and many businesses closed down immediately. Portugal's hasty withdrawal was followed by chaos as the MPLA, UNITA and FNLA[7] hammered out who was to run the country. The MPLA won the contest and quickly gained the backing of the Soviet Union and its ally, Cuba. UNITA responded by launching a war that was to last until 2002, when its leader Jonas Savimbi was killed. Those long years of war saw the country decline into turmoil, as millions of people were killed or maimed by bullets, bombs, landmines or famine and poverty. Less conspicuous was the increasing theft of public money through rampant corruption. Even though the

The armed struggle against Portugal's colonial rule launched in 1961 came to an end with the independence of Angola in 1975. Much more bloodshed was to follow over the next 26 years.

There are perhaps more landmines than people in the Angolan catchment. The mines are now long forgotten by the UNITA, FAPLA, Cuban and South African forces that planted them over the past 30 years, a legacy that will remain a threat for many years to come.

war was fought under political banners, it was really a contest to enrich the leaders of the parties, especially to control and pocket massive profits from diamonds and oil. The war was thus one in which power, people and resources were exploited for the personal gain of a handful.

There was a brief period of peace in 1992 during the run-up to Angola's first elections, but worse fighting followed when UNITA rejected the results of the election. Although UNITA's stronghold was amongst the Ovimbundu people in the central highlands, hundreds of thousands of soldiers, supporters and families were pulled south into Kuando Kubango, the province that makes up most of the catchment of the Okavango. The catchment thus became a UNITA stronghold, and Menongue was the only town held by government forces for many years. Government forces steadily gained ground in south-eastern Angola during the 1990s, eventually taking control of the border area between Namibia and Angola. UNITA people in the area were now trapped, and many turned to theft and

The Angolan catchment is replete with images of war and inhumanity, of desolation and neglect that create a dramatic contrast between the spending of billions of US dollars on sophisticated military technology and the absence of investment in social development. Tanks litter the surrounds of Cuito Cuanavale, remnants of the Battle of Cuito Cuanavale on 23 March 1988 when the Cuban and Angolan army repelled South African and UNITA forces. This was the second largest artillery battle in Africa; the biggest was at El Alamein, Egypt, during World War II.

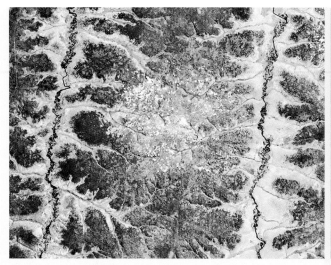
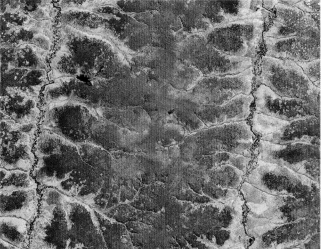

People have come and gone. The two satellite images give an example of how a whole town disappeared between the early 1990s (on the left, as indicated by the many fields and the bright white town centre) and 2000 when the image to the right was taken. The village spanned an area about 10 kilometres across and was home to hundreds of people, now displaced as a result of the civil war. The town of Chitembo lies 20 kilometres to the north-east, across the Cuchi River, while the river to the west is the Cutato. On the other hand, very large numbers of Angolans moved to Namibia, both before and during the civil war, one reason why there was such a dramatic increase in the amount of land cleared for crops between 1943 and 1996 in Kavango, as shown in the two maps below.

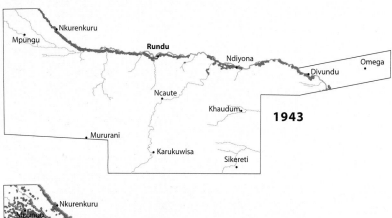
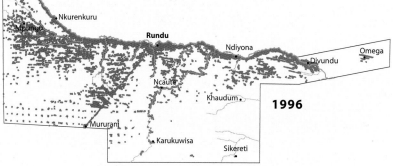

Right: scars of war in downtown Menongue, a town always held by the Angolan government forces but often bombed and besieged by UNITA.

murder. Angolan government troops were allowed to pursue their quarry from the Namibian side and a period of unrest and attacks broke out, causing an enormous decline in tourism and other economic activity in Kavango (see page 122).

What was the effect of civil war on the Basin area in Angola? Foremost was the damage to human life. No one will know how many people were killed, but landmines maimed thousands of people in the catchment. Huge numbers of people were also displaced, either forced away by soldiers or, more voluntarily, to seek a better life (see page 129). Both government and UNITA forces closed down and sometimes burnt whole villages. Landmines were planted around many remaining villages and towns, both by UNITA and government forces to keep each other out. People either fled into the bush or were trucked into towns. Tens of thousands of people settled in Namibia. Much of the infrastructure in the catchment was lost: bridges across most of the rivers, most schools, clinics and other services. The railway line to Menongue ceased to exist, and only a few roads are now free of mines. Perhaps millions of landmines lie hidden along roads and around villages and towns, limiting the physical movement of people but also dampening initiatives for development.

The war and high level of corruption has also cost Angola hundreds of billions of dollars, money that could be spent on development in the catchment. Even though the Angolan government may now allocate funds quite generously to the area (partly to win support from what was UNITA territory), there are far fewer people in the Basin than in the rest of the country. Most development funds will therefore be spent elsewhere in Angola. Finally, there has been a complete loss of social development and order. A whole generation of people has been displaced, literally and figuratively. Most Angolans have a history characterized by exploitation on a scale that few outsiders will appreciate: the mistreatment of millions of people over the last three decades, and for hundreds of years before that.

Ngamiland in Botswana and Kavango in Namibia have had a much more rosy recent history. Both countries have devoted large sums of money to rural development in both areas, most funds going to education and health services, roads, telecommunications, transport infrastructure and small-scale agriculture. Botswana has not lately entertained any plans to develop large-scale farms around the Delta, but many Namibians see the Kavango river valley as a potential bread-basket to make the country self sufficient in food production. Several large farms have thus been planned (see page 163).

Both Ngamiland and Kavango have also seen an enormous growth in economic activity based on the natural resources and beauty of the Okavango, for example through tourism, hunting and a variety of support services (see page 120). Both areas have thus capitalized on the comparative and competitive advantages that the river system offers. One challenge for those who plan and negotiate a good future for the waters of the Okavango is to see how such benefits can now be shared with the Angolan custodians of the river's source.

Key points

- Although people have lived in the Basin for hundreds of thousands of years, it has always been a difficult place to live because of disease, warfare, slavery and, in many areas, poor soils and low rainfall.
- Most people now living in the Basin are descended from recent immigrants usually pushed out of other areas in Angola, Botswana and Namibia.
- The Basin was unknown to the outside world until the mid-1800s and thereafter was generally ignored and treated as a desolate area. Only certain parts of the Basin have been developed in recent years.
- The cumulative effects of centuries of slavery, the recent civil war and corruption have damaged Angolan society enormously.

Important events

- Before 500: Sparsely populated by people living as hunters and gatherers
- 500s: Start of crop and cattle farming, iron work
- 1483: Diogo Cão is first European to visit Angola
- 1500–1850: Large-scale export of slaves
- Mid-1800s: Okavango river system becomes known to outside world; 1849 – David Livingstone visited Lake Ngami, 1859 – Charles John Andersson reached Okavango River near Nkurenkuru, and 1877 – Alexandre Serpa Pinto explored upper reaches of the river system
- 1884–1890s: Formal colonial territories are established in Angola, Namibia and Botswana
- 1966: Botswana becomes independent from Britain
- 1961–1975: Liberation war in Angola
- 1975: Angola becomes independent from Portugal
- 1976–2002: Civil war in Angola
- 1966–1989: Liberation war in Namibia
- 1990: Namibia becomes independent from South Africa

4

CLIMATE

Driving rains, drying sunshine

Advancing clouds signal the approach of rain
and new flows of water into the Okavango.

THE OKAVANGO BASIN'S climate changes gradually from north to south, following the same trend as the river as it flows from top to bottom and higher to lower elevations. Thus, rainfall is higher in the north where the air is more humid, cloud cover is greater and evaporation rates are lower than in the southern areas around the Okavango Delta. The steady southward changes in these three features mean that the river flows progressively into drier country. In fact, the river becomes more of an oasis to the south where the surrounding environment becomes increasingly arid. All of this gives the water increasing value to people, plants and animals in the south.

These trends result from interplay between the two major climate systems that affect the Basin's climate. The first is the Inter-tropical Convergence Zone (ITCZ), which brings in moisture from the north. Northern areas in the Basin thus receive more and earlier rain. Less and less moisture remains as the tropical air moves south, resulting in reduced cloud cover and rainfall, and higher solar radiation and rates of evaporation. The zone moves southwards early in the summer and back north in autumn, and this is why almost all rain falls during the summer. Most moisture in the ITCZ feeds into equatorial Africa from south-easterly Indian Ocean trade winds, but moist air also blows into the Zone from the Atlantic across the Congo Basin and northern Angola and down towards the highlands in the upper catchment.

A second climate system counteracts the flow of moisture from the ITCZ. This is the zone of high-pressure anticyclone cells that lie to the south. The cells also move north and south, bringing cool and dry air to southern Africa. Interactions between the anti-cyclonic cells and the ITCZ amount to something of a contest, the southerly high-pressure cells feeding in dry air, which pushes away the warm and moist ITCZ air. The high-pressure cells shift north to dominate the Basin in winter but also during sporadic dry spells in summer, while wet summers occur when the ITCZ has pushed far south.

The rains

Rain usually falls in strong and localized showers accompanied by thunderstorms, often in the afternoon after a steady buildup of clouds during the morning. Average totals per season in the highest areas of the catchment are over 1,300 mm. Since average seasonal or annual totals around Maun are approximately 450 mm, there is a three-fold decline in rainfall from north to south **(Figure 11)**. Note that, for purposes of

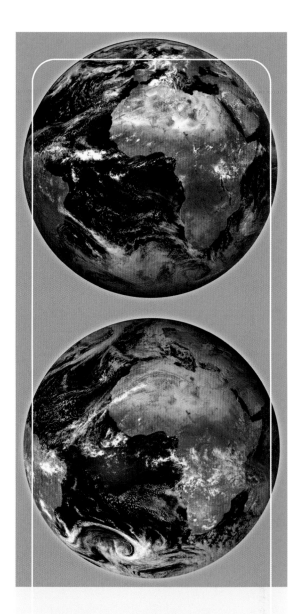

Little remains of the Intertropical Convergence Zone in winter when its band of moisture-bearing clouds has shifted well to the north, as shown in this satellite image taken in May 2003 (top). Clear, dry and cool air has then been driven into southern Africa by subtropical high-pressure air systems. The image below, taken in February 2003, reflects conditions in summer when the ITCZ and its rain-bearing clouds have moved well south. It is under these conditions that the Basin receives rain to add to the flow of water in the rivers of the Okavango.

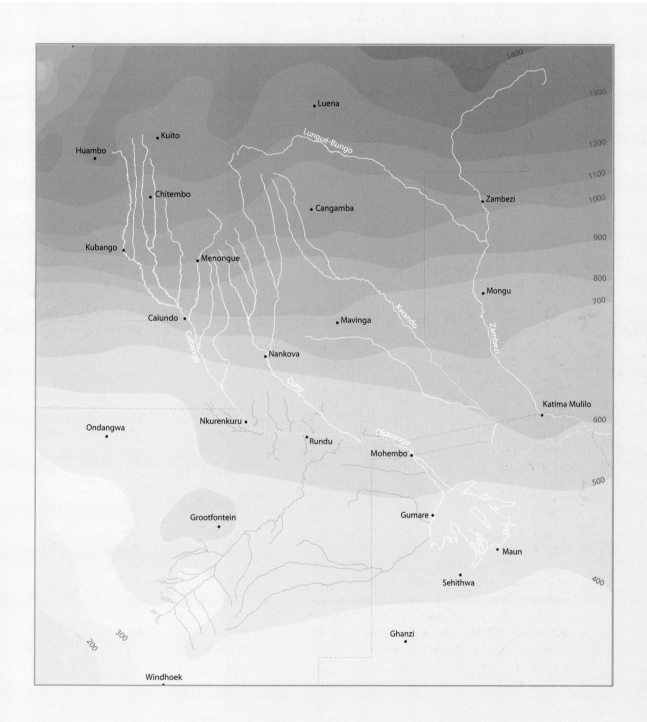

Figure 11

There is a steady gradient of rainfall across the Basin from areas in the north to those in the southern parts of the Delta. The highest totals of over 1,300 mm per season fall near Huambo, more than double the average of 560 mm at Rundu in the middle of the Basin and three times more than the average of 450 mm at Maun. All the perennial tributaries (white lines) have their origins in areas that receive more than 700 mm, while all the dry tributaries (brown lines) drain more arid areas.[1]

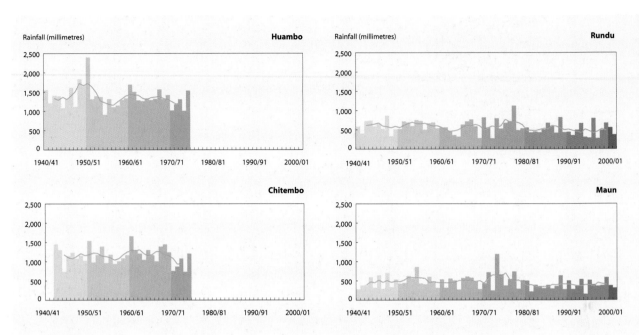

Figure 12

Rainfall varies greatly from season to season, as shown in these graphs of totals recorded over the past 60 years at Huambo, Chitembo, Rundu and Maun. The highest and lowest totals ever recorded during the years covered by these records are: Huambo: 2,350 and 962 mm, Chitembo: 1,849 and 814 mm, Rundu: 1,121 and 274 mm, and Maun: 1,186 and 151 mm. There are no figures over the past 27 years for Huambo and Chitembo because most weather stations closed after Angola's independence in 1975. The brown lines are moving averages.

measuring rainfall, a season lasts 12 months from July of one year to June of the next year.

These averages hide the obvious fact that rainfall varies from season to season, a point made clear by the graphs of seasonal totals at Huambo, Chitembo, Rundu and Maun (**Figure 12**). However, moving averages in the graphs also reveal some longer cycles, particularly the fact that the 1960s, 1980s and most of the 1990s were considerably drier than the 1950s and 1970s. Rainfall is much more variable – and therefore less reliable and predictable – in the southern part of the Basin than in the north (**Figure 13**). Natural vegetation and crop growth in the southern areas is thus limited both by shortages of rainfall and more frequent extreme scarcities. Some of these may be so severe that they are called droughts, and farmers may become eligible for government assistance. Droughts are, however, often proclaimed rather too readily. For example, 27 of the 33 years between 1964 and 1997 were declared as drought years in Botswana where dry periods are certainly a regular and normal occurrence.[2]

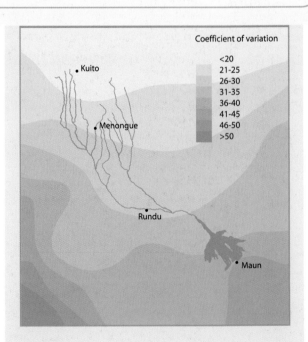

Figure 13

Rainfall in the southern areas of the Basin is much more variable than in the northern catchment. The co-efficient of variation of rainfall is about twice as high in the south as in the north.[3]

Early morning mists fill the valley of the Cuebe River near Menongue.

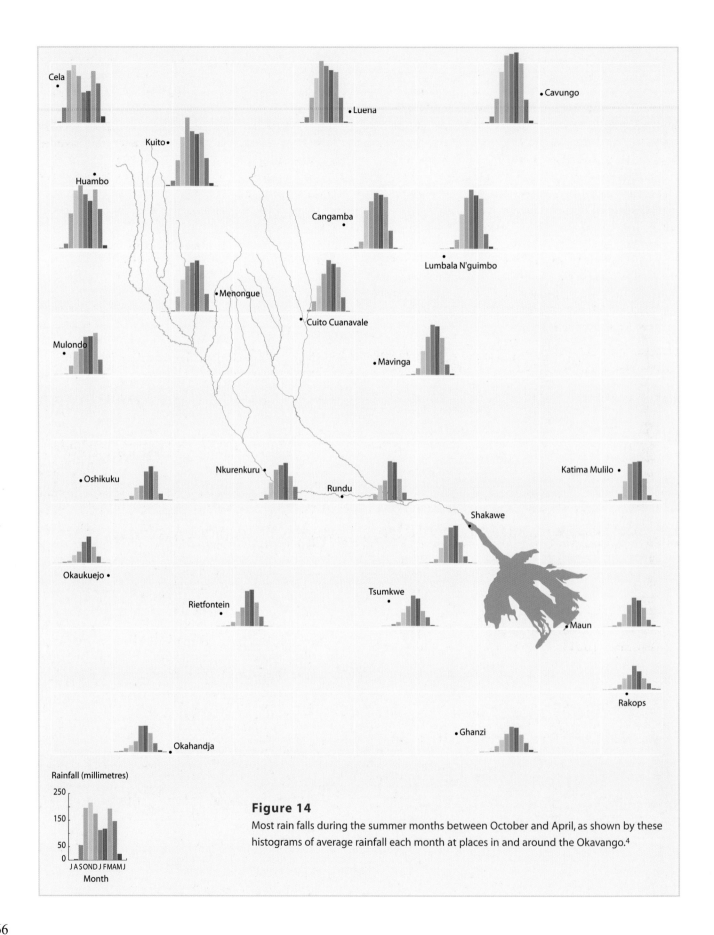

Cela

Luena

Cavungo

Kuito

Huambo

Cangamba

Menongue

Lumbala N'guimbo

Cuito Cuanavale

Mulondo

Mavinga

Oshikuku

Nkurenkuru

Rundu

Katima Mulilo

Shakawe

Okaukuejo

Rietfontein

Tsumkwe

Maun

Rakops

Okahandja

Ghanzi

Rainfall (millimetres)

250
150
50
0

J A S O N D J F M A M J

Month

Figure 14

Most rain falls during the summer months between October and April, as shown by these histograms of average rainfall each month at places in and around the Okavango.[4]

Over much of the northern catchment the rains are also spread fairly evenly over the summer months, while falls are more concentrated in January and February further south **(Figure 14)**. However, there are two peaks in the northern-most areas: one in November and December and the other in March and April. The two peaks correspond with the periods when the ITCZ passes overhead, first on its way south early in the summer and then on its return north in March and April. During the trough in January and February the Zone of moisture is usually further south, and it is then that Kavango and Ngamiland receive the best falls of rain.

Levels of humidity are greatest during the rainy season, especially between January and March, and the air is generally much more humid in the northern than in the southern regions. The air is driest during the heat of the day in late winter and early summer, when afternoon humidity levels typically range between 10 and 20% in Kavango and Ngamiland.

The flow of water is of course only possible because of abundant rainfall in the northern catchment. However, the river valleys as we see them now were probably largely formed during periods of much higher rainfall, for example those occurring in about 23,000 year cycles over the past 200,000 years **(Figure 15)**. Rainfall during the wettest cycles was often several times higher than the averages of today. This is when water would have carved the fossil drainage lines such as the Omatako and Nxamasere or Khaudum. By contrast, some of the rivers might have been completely covered up by sand during the driest of cycles. Average rainfall was then two or three times less than it is now and much of the area was covered in sand dunes (see **Figure 3** on page 33).

During much drier periods, the Okavango Delta might have looked like this salt-encrusted 'backwater' of the Makgadikgadi Pans.

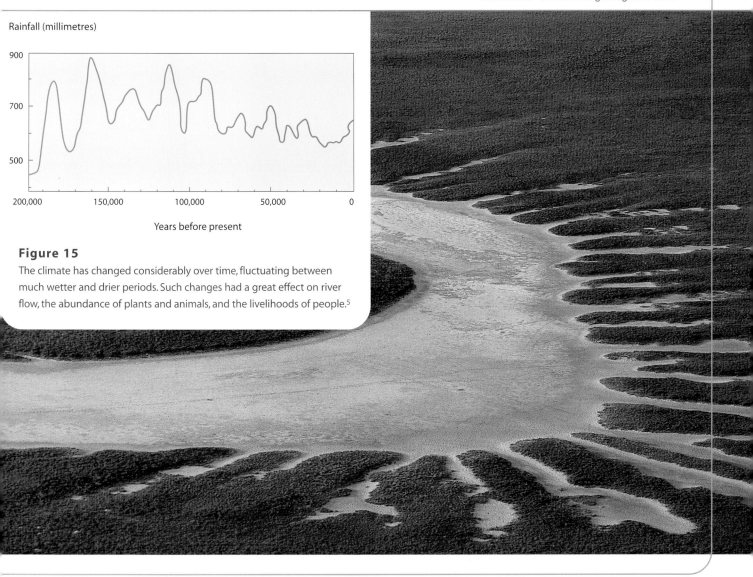

Rainfall (millimetres)

Years before present

Figure 15
The climate has changed considerably over time, fluctuating between much wetter and drier periods. Such changes had a great effect on river flow, the abundance of plants and animals, and the livelihoods of people.[5]

Degrees Celsius   **Rundu**

Degrees Celsius   **Maun**

Figure 16

Average daily maximum temperatures vary from 30 to 35° C during the months of October to January at Rundu and Maun. Thereafter, increasing cloud cover and rainfall lowers temperatures during the later summer months. Average minimum temperatures fall to about 7° C in the coldest months of June and July.[6]

Most rain in the Basin falls during afternoon thunderstorms.

Heat and wind

The Basin is characterized throughout by warm or hot conditions during most of the year and for much of every day **(Figure 16)**. Annual temperatures throughout the area average about 20° C, increasing by two or three degrees from north to south as a result of higher solar radiation in the southern areas. Winter nights and early mornings can be cold anywhere, but especially so in low-lying river valleys. Occasional frost occurs in such low-lying areas, sometimes frequently enough in the Angolan highlands to limit the growth of crops.

Although strong gusts blow during occasional storms, wind speeds are very low for most of the time across the Basin. In fact, it is completely calm for much of the time. For example, no wind was recorded for over half the time in most months at Rundu.

Evaporation varies from the highest rates of water loss in the south to much lower rates of water loss in the north **(Figure 17)**. Several times more water evaporates each year than is received by rain in most areas, which means that there are considerable overall deficits of water. Thus, the amounts of water lost to the atmosphere are higher in all months than the water received by rainfall at Maun and Rundu. At Menongue, by contrast, more water falls as rain than evaporates between December and March.

Figure 17
The highest rates of evaporation are in August, September and October when temperatures are high, there is little moisture in the air and it is often more windy than at other times of the year. Lower rates of water loss in mid-summer are due to the higher humidity and the cooler conditions brought about by cloud cover. Total average rates of evaporation per year at these three places were: Menongue: 1,924 mm, Rundu: 2,549 mm and Maun: 2,851 mm. Note that these rates are recorded on standard size evaporation pans, and actual rates of water loss over open stretches of water are generally about 30% lower than pan measurements.[7]

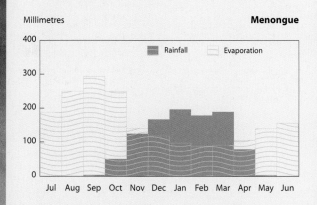

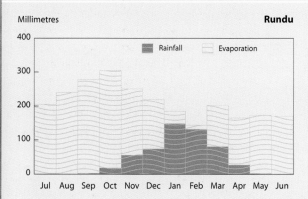

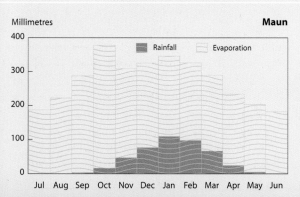

Key points

- Annual rainfall at the top of the catchment is about three times higher than that at the Delta.
- Most rain falls during summer between October and April in the northern catchment and from December to March in the south.
- The timing and amount of rainfall varies greatly from year to year, month to month and day to day. Dry spells occur regularly, especially in the southern Basin.
- Rainfall was generally low during the 1960s, 1980s and 1990s and higher in the 1950s and 1970s.
- Temperatures increase rapidly from the coldest months of June and July to the warmest month of October.
- Between two and three metres of water is potentially lost each year as a result of high evaporation rates.
- Winds are generally light, and it is completely calm for much of the time.

5

THE RIVER

Meandering across the Kalahari

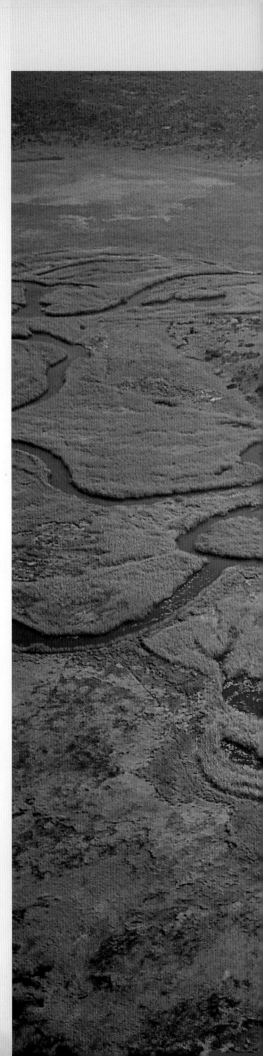

Convoluted meanders and horseshoe lakes on the Cutato River.

WATER COLLECTS in a large catchment area of about 111,000 square kilometres (km²), then flows hundreds of kilometres with no further inflow before finally dispersing in an alluvial fan that now covers up to 40,000 km². This is the essence of the Okavango, and very few rivers in the world work like this! The active catchment area lies wholly in Angola and is thus distinctly separated from the alluvial fan in Botswana, called the Okavango Delta.

The network of Okavango rivers sits squarely in the centre of southern Africa, where it is surrounded by other river systems that drain away east to the Indian Ocean or west to the Atlantic Ocean. The Okavango – and the Kwando just to the east – are unusual as they are the only major perennial rivers south of the equator that do not drain into the sea. Both rivers come to an end in the centre of the Kalahari Basin, a vast shallow depression of sand stretching across much of the centre of southern Africa (**Figure 18**).

Several other features make the waters of the Okavango special. First, the Delta is the largest wetland in southern Africa, and being in the centre of a vast arid area in the Kalahari gives it extra significance, rather like the value of a huge oasis. Secondly, the Delta is regarded as one of the most pristine wetlands in the world because it has been so little affected by humans. Few chemicals pollute its water, damming or channeling do not change the flow of water to any extent, and natural vegetation in the Delta is largely intact. In fact, many of the rivers in its catchment area in Angola are equally pristine. Thirdly, the river water is particularly clean and pure because most of the catchment areas drain Kalahari sands (see page 33) and the tributaries filter through vast areas of floodplains and marshes in Angola.

The Okavango Basin area on which we focus here is limited to the active catchment area from which water drains and the zone immediately around the flowing rivers and Delta. Some people choose to define the Basin as covering a much larger area (**Figure 19**) to include the fossil drainage lines in Namibia, Botswana and Zimbabwe, and also the Makgadikgadi Pans as an area into which Okavango water flowed during much wetter periods. In Angola, the catchment is made up of the western Cubango sub-Basin, consisting of the Cubango, Cutato, Cuchi, Cacuchi, Cuelei, Cuebe, Cueio and Cuatir Rivers. These join to form the Cubango in Angola, later called the Okavango in Namibia and Botswana. The eastern or Cuito sub-Basin consists of the Luassinga, Longa, Cuiriri, Cuito and Cuanavale Rivers – all of which feed the Cuito before its junction with the Okavango on the Angola/Namibia border. Water is distributed across the alluvial fan or Okavango Delta along three main channels: the Thaoge, Jao and Nqoga.

Much the largest part of the active Basin is in Angola, and the whole Basin extends across almost nine degrees of latitude between 12 and 21ºS. The main river after which the Basin is named (first as the Cubango in Angola, then as the Okavango and finally through the Delta to Maun) covers a straight-line distance of about 1,900 kilometres. This is just a rough indication of the river system's length because most of the rivers spend more time meandering than flowing directly to the south. Their waterways therefore cover many thousands of kilometres. **Figure 20** and the table on page 74 show the areas covered by the catchment areas of all the major rivers in Angola, and the remaining zones in and around the river system in Kavango and Ngamiland.

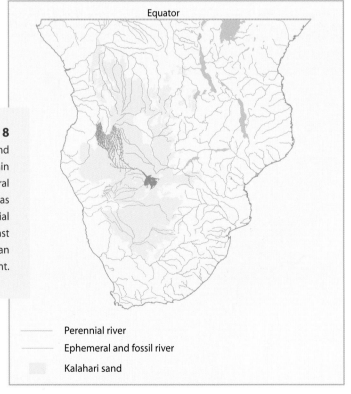

Figure 18
The Okavango and Kwando rivers drain into the central Kalahari Basin whereas all other perennial rivers flow to the coast of the African continent.

Equator

—— Perennial river
—— Ephemeral and fossil river
 Kalahari sand

Figure 19

The Okavango Basin forms part of a large drainage area in the central Kalahari. Much of that area is now dry but a great deal of water flowed there during wetter periods long ago (see page 67). Some water still flows along ephemeral rivers after heavy rains, but the fossil rivers have not flowed into the Okavango in living memory. Many of the rivers were also connected during wetter times when Okavango water could flow into the Kwando, Chobe and then the Zambezi, and also to the Makgadikgadi Pans. The Zambezi River drained into eastern Botswana and, together with the Okavango and Kwando, produced a lake covering about 60,000 km² in and around the Makgadikgadi Pans. This is five times bigger than the largest area flooded in the Delta in recent decades. Later on, probably within the last two million years, the upper Zambezi was captured and diverted along its present course to the Mozambique coast.[1]

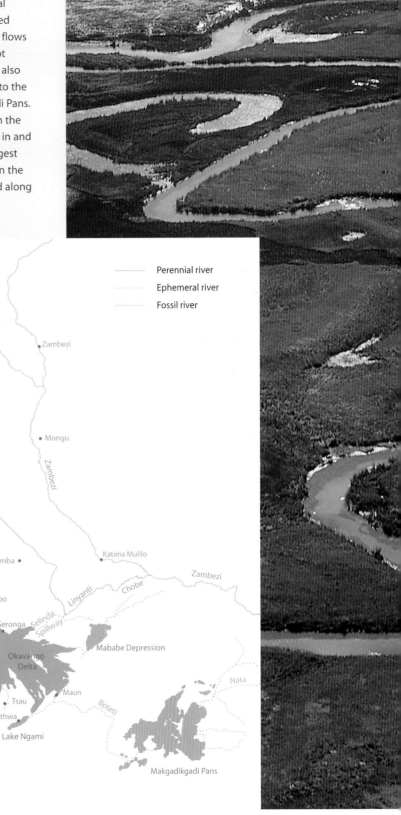

Crystal clear, pristine waters of the Cuebe River upstream of Menongue.

Perennial river
Ephemeral river
Fossil river

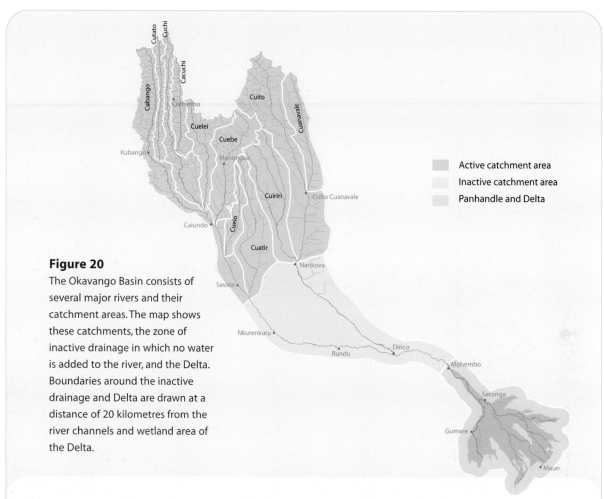

Figure 20

The Okavango Basin consists of several major rivers and their catchment areas. The map shows these catchments, the zone of inactive drainage in which no water is added to the river, and the Delta. Boundaries around the inactive drainage and Delta are drawn at a distance of 20 kilometres from the river channels and wetland area of the Delta.

The size, average rainfall and approximate run-off in the catchment area of the major rivers.[2]

River or zone	Area (square (kilometres)	Average rainfall (millimetres)	Average run off (cubic kilometres)	Percentage of total input
Cubango[a]	14,400	1,064	1.290	15%
Cutato	4,200	1,166	0.420	6%
Cuchi[b]	8,900	1,071	0.820	10%
Cacuchi	4,800	1,150	0.470	5%
Cuelei	7,500	1,065	0.690	6%
Cuebe	11,200	992	0.960	10%
Cuatir	11,600	750	0.750	5%
Cueio	3,700	829	0.260	3%
Cuiriri[c]	12,900	876	0.980	10%
Cuito[d]	24,300	975	2.060	22%
Cuanavale	7,750	1,018	0.680	7%
Total active catchment	**111,250**	**978**	**9.380**	**100%**
Inactive drainage area[e]	45,000	571	0	0
Delta	35,300	469	0	0

a Includes its own catchment area and areas downstream of the junctions of the Cutato, Cuchi, Cacuchi, Cuelei, Cuebe and Cueio rivers.

b Includes its own catchment and the area downstream of the junction of the Cacuchi.

c The Cuiriri includes the Luassinga and Longa rivers.

d Includes its own catchment and the area downstream of the junction of the Cuanavale.

e The area from which there is no active drainage surrounding the rivers in southern Angola and Namibia.

The Cuito meanders sideways as much as flowing south to its confluence with the Cubango/Okavango.

The Nxamasere or Khaudum fossil drainage course (left) *runs from Kavango east to the Delta, while the Selinda Spillway* (right) *connects the Delta with the mini-delta formed as the Kwando River runs up against the Linyanti Fault. Depending on water levels during very wet periods, water can flow from the Kwando to the Delta – or vice versa.*

The largest separate river catchments are those of the Cuito, Cuiriri and Cuatir, while the Cutato, Cubango and Cuchi catchments have the highest rainfalls. The active catchment areas of the Cubango and Cuito, together with their major river tributaries, cover areas of 66,300 and 44,950 km², respectively. Turning to the fossil and ephemeral river courses **(Figure 19)**, the Boteti River still carries overflow from the Delta from time to time. For example, it had substantial flows during the 1950s, 1960s and 1970s when rainfall was generally higher than in the drier 1980s and 1990s. The Nata River sometimes flows from south-western Zimbabwe into Sua Pan in the Makgadikgadi. The longest of the fossil drainages are the Omatako (635 kilometres from its source near the Omatako Hills to its confluence at Ndonga), the Eiseb and Nxamasere (also called the Khaudum). Many shorter fossil rivers or omurambas drain from the south or north into the Okavango where it forms the Angola/Namibia border. None of these river courses has flowed any distance in recorded history.

Tributaries and distributaries

The broad pattern of water flow in the Okavango should be clear: water collects in the catchment, flows down the Cubango, Okavango and Cuito for several hundred kilometres, and is then distributed across the Delta. An important point is that all water flowing into Botswana comes originally from Angola, and the river simply flows through Namibia – rather like a canal. But what are the details of where the water assembles in Angola and how it disperses in Botswana?

Inflows are fairly evenly spread across the catchment from east to west. As a percentage of all water entering the Delta, the greatest flows are provided by the Cuito (22%), Cubango (14%), Cuebe (10%) and Cuiriri (10%).[3] Although the Cutato, Cuchi, Cacuchi and Cuanavale also drain high rainfall areas, their catchments are smaller, while the Cuelei, Cueio and Cuatir have smaller catchments in rather drier areas. From these figures and water flow measurements at Rundu (before the Cuito) and Mohembo (after the confluence), about 55% of all water flowing into the Delta comes down the Cubango/Okavango while the Cuito and its tributaries provides 45%. Water flow is thus at a maximum between the confluence of the Cuito and Mohembo, a distance of about 140 kilometres.

Dispersal of the river begins at the top of the Panhandle, and an estimated 40% of the total volume of water leaks into the surrounding swamps by the time the river leaves the Panhandle. The remaining 60% flows into the head of the alluvial fan from where it is distributed down three main channels. The Nqoga channel takes 63% of water entering the fan, the Jao 21% and the Thaoge 16%. Much more water thus flows east along the Nqoga from where water leaks and disperses further along the Maunachira, Mboroga and Santantidibe distributary channels. In years of high flow, floodwaters may reach the Kunyere and Thamalakane rivers in the far south-east. And when levels are really high, the two rivers flow south-westwards bringing water to Lake Ngami and the Boteti River.

The average volume of river water coming into the Delta each year is about 9.4 cubic kilometres, and to this is added about another 3.2 cubic kilometres of rain water that falls directly on the Delta each year.[4] The total input of water to the Delta is thus about 12.6 cubic kilometres, a volume that would cover an area of 100 by 126 kilometres in one metre of water.

An estimated 96% of all water entering the Delta as river water and direct rainfall is lost by evapotranspiration. This includes evaporation of water directly into the atmosphere and indirectly through transpiration by plants. Water loss through transpiration probably exceeds evaporation, especially during the summer growing season and in the permanent swamps. About another 2.5% of all water in the Delta seeps away into groundwater aquifers, while the remaining 1.5% flows out of the system along the Boteti River. The 1.5% is an average, however, comprising many years in which there is no outflow and others when substantial volumes make their way down the Boteti.[5]

Changing rivers

Along its course, the river system has many different forms: as cascading flows, sluggish meanders, or seepage through expansive floodplains, dense reed beds and swamplands. These are the forms seen today. But it is important to recall that the structures of the rivers, especially the valleys and floodplains through which they flow, evolved over periods of hundreds of thousands or millions of years. Moreover, many of the formations developed during periods of much higher rainfall (see page 67) when the rivers carried several times more water than they do today. These effects would have been substantial because of the shallow gradient of most rivers. For example, along stretches now characterized by floodplains,

the river water would have spread across much bigger areas for longer periods, rather than draining away rapidly as would happen along a steep river gradient. The mantle of Kalahari sand would also have been stripped away more rapidly during periods of high rainfall. It was doubtless those large flows that formed the broad river valleys that are now several kilometres wide in Angola and Kavango. Similarly, many other rivers would have flowed during the wetter periods. The remains of some of these are clearly visible today as fossil rivers while others have been covered up by wind-blown sand during recent arid periods.

For stretches and areas of active flow, six different formations are recognized and described here: Incised Valleys, Valley Marshlands, Floodplain Valleys, the Panhandle, Permanent Swamps, and Seasonal Swamps (**Figure 21**). These are described and illustrated on the following pages. The first three formations encompass areas of active river flow in Angola and Namibia. Most Incised Valleys and all the Valley Marshlands are in the western highlands of the catchment where they cut through and across various bedrock formations (see page 33). Their main courses run parallel and due south, and are fed by dense networks of hundreds of tiny tributaries. Run-off from the rivers is relatively rapid and much more variable than in the Floodplain Valleys that characterize the eastern areas of the Angolan catchment. These eastern valleys sweep across large areas of Kalahari sand, and the only relatively dense network of tributaries is in the headwaters of the Cuito. Over most of the remaining areas between the Floodplain Valleys the landscape is very even, and there are vast areas in which there are no active drainage lines.

The remaining three formations are in the Delta. The first is the Panhandle with a gradient of 1:5,000, while the other two (Permanent Swamps and Seasonal Swamps) are in the slightly steeper alluvial fan with a gradient of 1:3,300. Floodplains, swamps and tongues of sandy ground separate the three main channels: the Thaoge, Jao and the Nqoga. The exact margins of the whole Delta are difficult to define because the extent of flooding varies from year to year, and some outlying areas are only inundated in exceptional flood years.

Incised Valleys

Most of the tributaries in the north-western catchment flow along clearly defined V-shaped valleys, although the valleys are all shallow. While there are broad meanders in places, the meander is usually along a single channel. Incised Valleys predominate in areas where bedrock is exposed or the mantle of Kalahari sand is shallow. There are many short rapids or waterfalls along certain stretches, and the gradients are steeper than anywhere else in the whole Basin (see page 40). Vegetation in the valleys varies considerably: woodland extends right down to the river in many areas whereas elsewhere the rivers are surrounded by margins of grassland. In some places there is riparian forest or patches of floodplains or grasses, sedges or reeds. The Cubango/Okavango runs as an Incised Valley for most of its length and it is only west of Musese in Kavango that the river changes into a Floodplain Valley. Almost all tributaries of the Cubango, Cutato, Cuchi, Cacuchi, Cuelei and many of those flowing into the Cuebe are Incised Valleys. The bottoms of the great majority of these tributary valleys consist of permanently wet grassland, or bog, on either side of small streams. This is true of even the smallest valleys and so these wet grasslands provide seepage of water into the rivers throughout the year.

Valley Marshlands

These swampy areas are restricted to the north-western catchment and are especially common along the Cutato, Cuchi and Cacuchi rivers. It appears that the

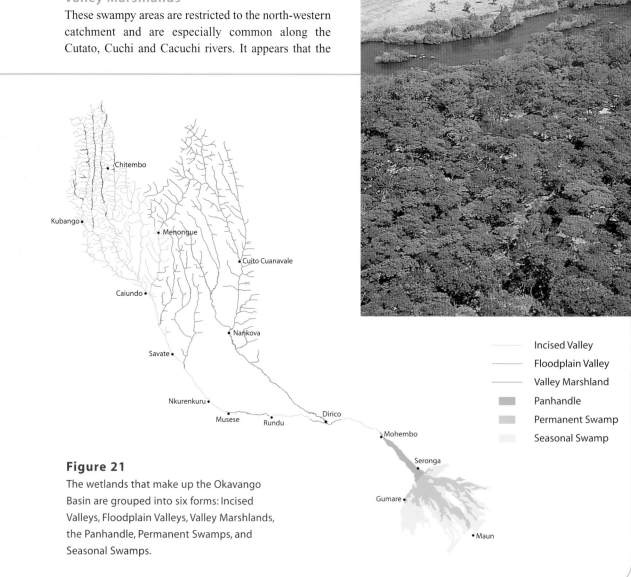

Figure 21
The wetlands that make up the Okavango Basin are grouped into six forms: Incised Valleys, Floodplain Valleys, Valley Marshlands, the Panhandle, Permanent Swamps, and Seasonal Swamps.

———— Incised Valley
———— Floodplain Valley
———— Valley Marshland
Panhandle
Permanent Swamp
Seasonal Swamp

bottoms of Incised Valleys have been so filled with sediments that the gradient of the rivers has become much shallower. The rivers thus snake their way downstream through dense, tall *Phragmites* reed beds. Hundreds of ox-bow lakes and convoluted meanders characterize each stretch. The marshes are often several hundred metres in width and, cumulatively, they cover an area of several hundred square kilometres. One important effect of the reed beds is that they filter out nutrients, sediments and pollutants from upstream. The marshes also stabilize the flow of water by slowing surges of floodwater, but then also gradually releasing water from the inundated reed beds during drier times.

Floodplain Valleys

Most of these valleys are in the north-eastern areas of the Angolan catchment, although sections of the Okavango along the Angola/Namibia border share this structure. The valleys are extremely shallow and are generally several kilometres wide. River channels in the centre of the valleys follow broad meanders, in some places now cut off as ox-bow lakes. The channels are lined with expanses of sedges and other grasses that form a distinct floodplain of short vegetation. Beyond the floodplains is another wide area of short, dry grassland that extends up to the sharp edges of the flanking woodland. Few trees or other woody plants grow within the Floodplain Valleys, and it is their openness, short grasses and distinct margins of woodland that characterize them best.

The Panhandle

This is the beginning of the Delta. Although most people consider the Panhandle as starting at Mohembo, the feature really begins upstream in the Mahango Game Reserve from where it extends south to the Gumare Fault. Most of the water flow is along a single meandering channel surrounded by a broad area of marshes dominated by papyrus and reeds. Relative to the adjacent floodplains, the water level of the river becomes progressively elevated down the Panhandle, rising to about 60 centimetres higher than the surrounding swamps at the end of the Panhandle. This is because sediments deposited on the floor of the channel raise the waterway, but the dense growth of papyrus along its margins acts as a barrier through which water can only seep away slowly.

An Incised Valley on the Cubango River between Kubango and Caiundo (left) and a Valley Marshland along the Cutato River (below).

Permanent Swamps

The Permanent Swamps form the core of the alluvial fan and surround the three main channels (Nqoga, Jao and Thaoge) that distribute water across the fan. The swamps cover much of the upper northern and central areas of the Delta, where they extend over an area of 2,000 to 3,000 km². Seasonal Swamps cover the remaining southern, western and eastern areas. Many lakes (mostly ancient ox-bows) are dotted across the Permanent Swamps. Water flow is largely along channels from where the waters slowly leak through dense margins of plants into large expanses of papyrus, reeds and sedges. There are distinct zones of less dense vegetation away from the main channels because plants near the larger channels are first to absorb incoming nutrients and therefore grow best. Fewer nutrients remain available to plants growing further away, by contrast. Water levels in the Permanent Swamps are rather constant, unlike fluctuations of up to two metres during the year in the Panhandle.

A typical Floodplain Valley on the upper reaches of the Cuanavale River (left) and a broad view across the Panhandle (below).

Seasonal Swamps

Most floodwaters enter the Seasonal Swamps after filtering through the Permanent Swamps. The expanse of Seasonal Swamps varies greatly from year to year between 4,000 and 8,000 km², depending largely on the inflow from the Angolan catchment and local rainfall over the Delta. Unlike flows along channels in the Permanent Swamps, most water in the Seasonal Swamps flows as sheet flooding, the water spreading slowly across the gently undulating landscape. The water is usually less than half a metre deep, and many areas of higher ground therefore remain stranded as temporary islands during the floods. Plant communities are more diverse than elsewhere in the Delta because the Seasonal Swamps are subject to such a variety of flooding patterns, with different plant species favouring patches that vary according to the duration and depth of flooding.

Together with the Panhandle, the Permanent Swamps (right) *and Seasonal Swamps* (below) *form the largest RAMSAR wetland site in the world.*

Variable flows

Almost all river water originates as rain falling during the summer months (see page 66).[6] Peak flows are in March for rivers feeding the Cubango sub-Basin, while the highest flows only reach the lower Cuito in May **(Figure 22)**. The earlier March peak is due to rainwater draining quickly off basement rocks or the thin mantle of Kalahari sand and then flowing down relatively steep gradients in the west. The whole Cuito sub-Basin, by contrast, is characterized by much more stable, regular flows of water slowly seeping through the sands and flowing gradually along its meanders and filtering through the extensive floodplains that surround its rivers.

Although little water eventually finds its way to Maun, flows that turn the Thamalakane into an actual river usually peak in August. This is four months after the highest wave of water has entered the Panhandle. Water that has covered close to 1,000 kilometres from the headwaters of the Cubango to Mohembo in a

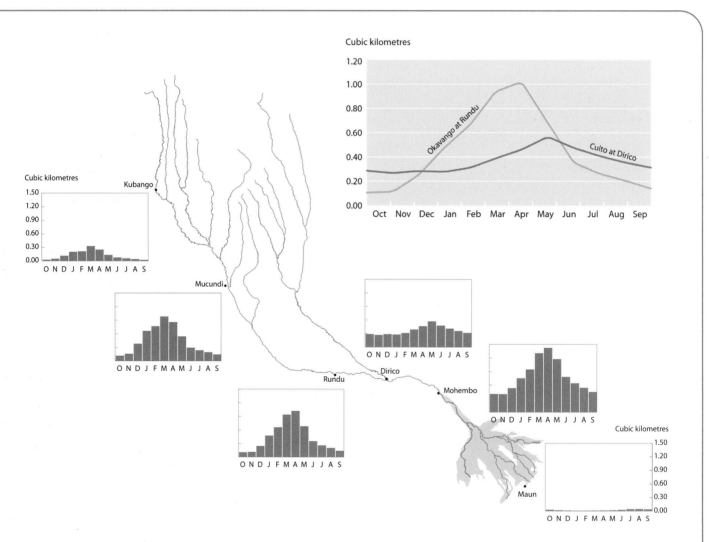

Figure 22

Most runoff in Angola is in March in the western Cubango sub-Basin and during May in the east along the lower Cuito. The time taken for Okavango water to flow from Rundu to Mohembo plus the effects of the later input from the Cuito means that peak flows enter Botswana in April. From there the waters take about four months to permeate through to Maun, where the highest flows are recorded in August. The inset graph also shows how the volume of water carried by the Okavango at Rundu is greater than that of the Cuito between January and May, but the Cuito provides more water during the rest of the year.[7]

month or two thus spends another four months creeping down to Maun 250 kilometres away. The slow passage of the flood across the Delta is due to several factors: the shallow gradient, seepage into the ground, water having to filter its way through vegetation, and the uneven landscape which means that upstream depressions first have to fill before the water moves on.

As another reflection of the more variable supply of water down the Cubango sub-Basin, the highest rate of flow ever recorded for the Okavango (962 cubic metres per second (m³/s)) is roughly 90 times greater than the lowest rate ever recorded (11 m³/s). The same figures for the Cuito vary by a factor of less than 10: from a high of between 550 and 600 m³/s to the lowest of 64 m³/s. The Cubango/Okavango also flows much more rapidly than the Cuito during annual floods: average rates of flow at Rundu in April are 401 m³/s, more than double average flow (175 m³/s) in the peak month of May on the Cuito at Dirico. In the summer months between January and May, total volumes carried by the Cubango/Okavango are greater than those in the Cuito, while the Cuito provides more water during the other seven months of the year **(Figure 22)**.

Flows along the Cubango/Okavango and Cuito subside each year to a fairly stable rate of discharge **(Figure 23)**. Thus, while flows in April fluctuate greatly from year to year as a result of

differences in rainfall and runoff, there is relatively little annual variation in October volumes. The only significant change is the lower flows in recent years due to lower rainfall (see page 88).

Annual flows (in cubic kilometres) per season at Rundu above the Cuito's confluence, below the Cuito at Mohembo and at Maun.[8]

Place and years of data	Average	Minimum (year)	Maximum (year)
Rundu (1945–2001)	5.207	2.260 (1971/72)	9.810 (1962/63)
Mohembo (1933–2001)	9.384	5.313 (1995/96)	15.977 (1967/68)
Maun (1951–1999)	0.271	0 (1995–1997)	1.174 (1954/55)

The differences between maximum and minimum volumes in the table are substantial – about four times at Rundu, three times at Mohembo, and hundreds of times at Maun – all largely reflecting how widely flows vary between high and low years, as shown by the year-to-year changes in **Figure 25**. However, several other factors play a role in determining levels

The Thamalakane near Maun is usually dry but it becomes a substantial waterway in those years when lots of water flows into the Delta.

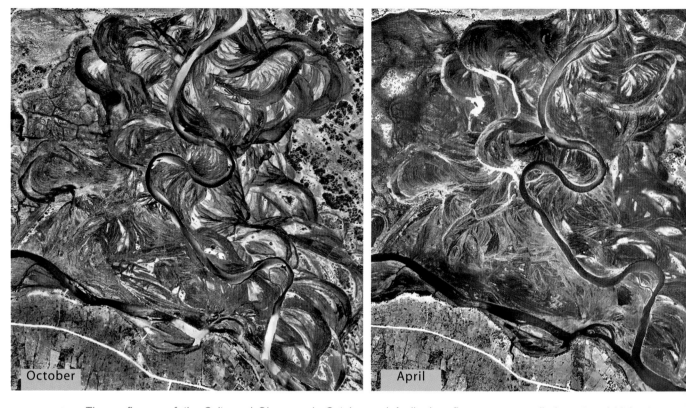

The confluence of the Cuito and Okavango in October and April when flows are generally lowest and highest, respectively. The curved patterns are scroll bars of sand deposits left as the rivers have meandered from side to side (above). A fish eagle overlooks the Panhandle, where biological production (and thus fish stocks) is highest because this is where most nutrients carried into the Delta are trapped (right).

of water flow reaching Maun and this is why there is a weak correlation between river levels at Maun and those upstream at Mohembo and Rundu.

Levels of water flow along the rivers naturally have a great impact on the size of areas flooded in the Delta. Examples of the extent of flooding in two years are given in **Figure 26**, one for 1995 (a dry year) and 2001 (a much wetter year). The examples are limited to years for which satellite images could be obtained to map areas of flooding. While 1995 had one of the lowest flows on record, the flow in 2001 was very much lower than many of those in the 1960s **(Figure 25)**. The largest extent of actual floodwater measured over the past three decades was 11,400 km² in June 1979. This was roughly double a maximum flood area of 5,100 km² in 1996, the driest recent year on record. The 11,400 km² of water was also about four times bigger than the smallest area of surface water recorded during the dry months: 2,450 km² in February 1996.[9]

Levels of flooding obviously depend on volumes of water inflow from Angola, but three more factors determine the degree of inundation in the Delta.[10] The first is local rainfall since an average of 25% of water in the Delta comes from rain falling directly on the

area. The percentage is higher in years with good local rainfall but low inflow, but then less when good inflows dominate the effect of rain on the Delta. However, rain is often very local and so heavy falls may flood certain areas while others stay dry. Rain falling on dry ground adds to the saturation of the soil, raises groundwater levels and allows floodwaters to proceed more rapidly. This introduces a second influence on the extent of flooding: the effect of flooding during the previous year on the degree of soil saturation and height of the water table. If the ground is already saturated and the water table high from good flows in the previous year, new floodwaters move along quickly, more water remains on the surface and bigger areas are flooded. The third factor is evaporation, with floodwaters remaining longer during times when rates of water loss are low. Total evaporation amounts to over 2,800 mm of water each year, but it is during the hot, often windy spring months of September and October that water is lost most rapidly (see page 69). Up to 10 mm may then evaporate every day, an effect that does much to dry up the Delta rapidly before the coming of the next year's flood.

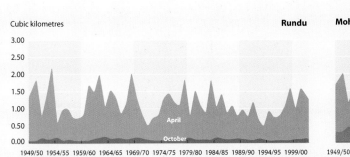

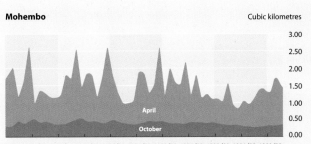

Figure 23

Compared to April, the volume of water carried in October is much lower but also much more stable than in April when flows fluctuate widely from year to year. The river also carries much more water at Mohembo during October than at Rundu because of the greater input of water from the Cuito during the drier months.[11]

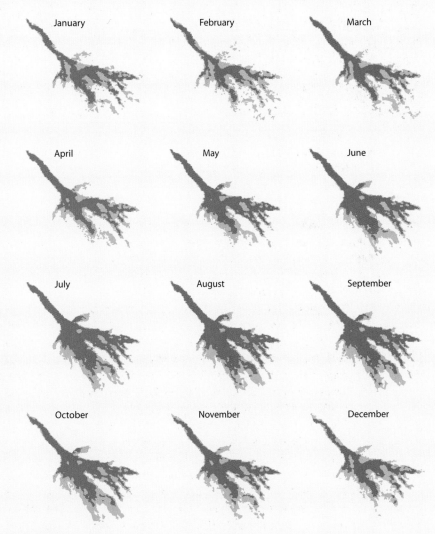

Figure 24

The annual flood slowly spreads across the Delta, areas of open water increasing month by month from March. On average, August is the month in which the extent of floodwaters is greatest. The maps show the average frequency of flooding each month. Dark blue areas are inundated more often than pale blue ones.[12]

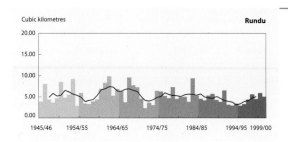

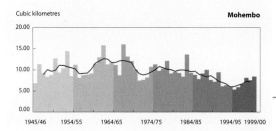

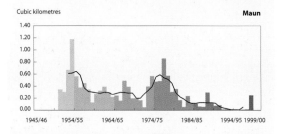

Figure 25

Volumes of water passing Rundu and Mohembo fluctuate greatly from year to year, but don't vary anything like as much as flows at Maun. Only in years with high flows and/or good rainfall over the Delta can Maun expect to see much water in the Thamalakane River. The columns show the actual values while the red lines are moving averages over five years to reflect longer-term changes, especially the lower flows in the 1980s and 1990s due to lower rainfall. The three histograms below show the number of years in which different flows were recorded.

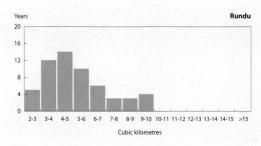

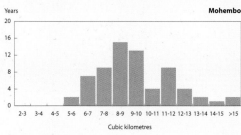

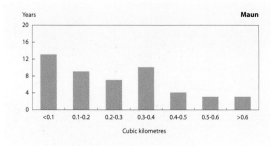

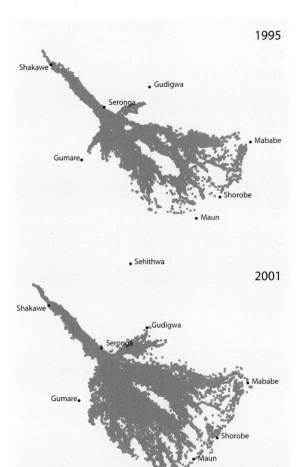

Figure 26

Differences in the extent of flooding have a great impact on life in the Delta, for example on the distribution and size of areas available for mammals to graze or fish to breed. The two maps show maximum flood areas during a dry year (1995) and a much wetter one (2001).

The dynamic Delta

Two circumstances are required for the formation of alluvial fans. The first is a landscape with a very shallow gradient, the kind of surface perhaps created in the rift valley between the Gumare and the Thamalakane faults (see page 35). The second is that river valley walls no longer confine the flow of water. Given these conditions, a river begins depositing sediments at the point where it starts flowing across a shallow surface. Water levels are raised by the accumulation of sediments and this forces the flow of water further outwards to lower-lying areas.

Although the biggest area covered by floodwater in the last 30 years was 11,400 km^2, sediments deposited by the river over thousands of years formed a larger alluvial fan that covers some 40,000 km^2 (see page 35). Much of this larger area was flooded during wetter periods when inflows were considerably greater. But the larger area of old sediments also reflects a fundamental feature of the Delta: that of continuing change in the distribution of water. Channels come and go, flowing here and then there as their current slows and then speeds off in new directions down new passages. As recently as 120 years ago, most water flowed to the southwestern areas along the Thaoge channel, and Lake Ngami was regularly filled by the Thaoge. Flows into the Thaoge largely dried up in about 1880, and the Thaoge is now a relative trickle that disperses far to the north of Ngami. The swamps that previously surrounded the Thaoge became vast areas of peat that burnt away over the years, turning the whole area into extensive grasslands.

Smoke from a smouldering peat fire that may burn over months, even years.

Such changes in the spread of water lead to another fundamental characteristic of the Delta: the enormous diversity of habitats produced by the changing presence and depth of water across this oasis. And from that variety of habitats follows the wealth of plants, animals and scenic beauty that give the Delta such great value. None of this would, of course, be possible without the ingredients that come flowing down the river from Angola: the water and the nutrients and sediments that it carries.

Water levels fluctuate by up to two metres between the highest and lowest flows at the top of the Panhandle, where the height, volume and speed of water flow entering the Delta is greatest. The water then disperses and fluctuations in level diminish as floodwaters percolate into the permanent swamps before spreading into the seasonal swamps. Larger areas are flooded and water remains longer in the seasonal swamps following good inflows. Moreover, plant growth is better and the underground water table rises in such 'good' years (see page 102).

Nutrients and sediments are the other main ingredients brought into the Delta, and it is these that have indeed built the whole alluvial fan. Salts make up a high proportion of the many different compounds carried down the Okavango, but water in the Delta is exceptionally clean and free of salts. This is remarkable because salts become concentrated in most wetlands in hot and arid areas, resulting in the formation of crusts of salty and infertile ground. Southern Africa has good examples of this in the Etosha and Makgadikgadi Pans. Why should the Delta water be so free of salts? The answer lies in the action of the rich plant life. Unlike saltpans, where water

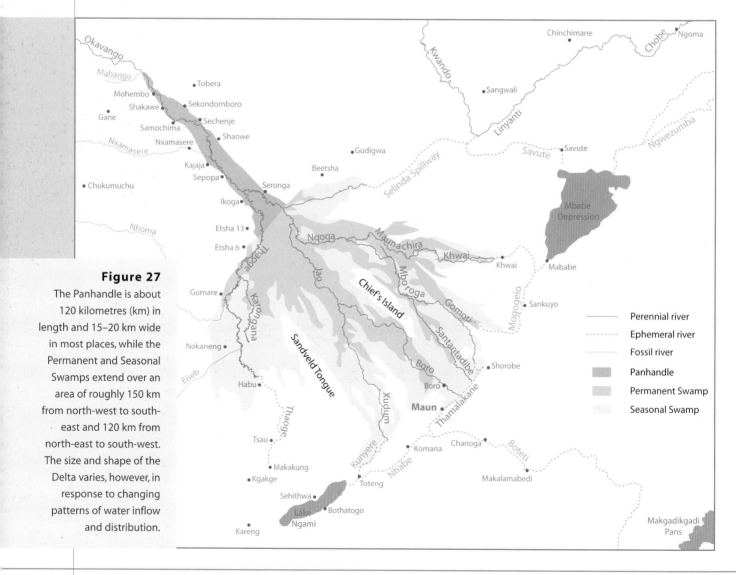

Figure 27

The Panhandle is about 120 kilometres (km) in length and 15–20 km wide in most places, while the Permanent and Seasonal Swamps extend over an area of roughly 150 km from north-west to south-east and 120 km from north-east to south-west. The size and shape of the Delta varies, however, in response to changing patterns of water inflow and distribution.

A channel, now choked with plant growth and abandoned, was raised above the surrounding floodwaters by the steady accumulation of sand on its bottom.

simply evaporates leaving behind any salt it carried, most water in the Delta does not evaporate. Rather, most is lost through the leaves of growing plants, a process called transpiration. As the plants draw up water through their roots, some salts are absorbed into the plant body while others remain in the ground. From here, the salts permeate into the groundwater below the Delta or become concentrated in the soils beneath the many islands. Indeed, the islands play a particularly important role in concentrating salts because trees growing on the islands draw water in towards them from the surrounding swamps. Salts carried by the water thus collect in the basal soils of the islands. The highest concentrations are in the island centres where so much salt aggregates that the soils eventually become too poisonous for plant growth.

Trees growing on islands transpire great quantities of water into the atmosphere, with the result that salts are concentrated on islands and thus removed from the Delta's waters. White centres to these islands mark patches of soils that are now so salty that no plants grow there (left). Zones of vegetation around channels in the Delta reflect the access that plants have to nutrients. Thus, plant growth is tallest close to the main channels because nutrients are more abundant than further away (below).

Each year, an estimated 170,000 tonnes of sand is carried down from the Angolan catchment into the Delta where it settles on the bottoms or beds of channels. This simple process of deposition is the main reason why flows switch from one direction or channel to another. The sand is largely rolled along the channel floors as so-called bed-load, and then settles once the speed of water flow is too slow to carry it further. The accumulating sand raises the levels of the channels, further reducing rates of flow and allowing more sand to settle. Papyrus growth also encroaches on the channels as water speeds drop, bringing the flow of water to a stop and eventually blocking the channels completely.

The diversity of habitats in the Delta is remarkably high, a quality that results in part from the presence of termites and hippos. There may be as many as 150,000 islands, particularly in the southern and eastern seasonal swamp areas, and perhaps 70% of all islands developed on original termite mounds (right).[13] Water seepage into swamp areas away from the main channels is accelerated by hippo trails (below). Once the bed of a main channel rises and water flow slows as a result of sand deposition, the main flow may switch down a hippo trail. The now fast flowing water can erode and widen the trail to form a completely new channel.

Rates of sand accumulation are substantial, perhaps as much as five centimetres per year or half a metre in 10 years. The channel margins of peat become increasingly dense and impenetrable. Water in a blocked channel can rise only so much before finally breaking through the sides of the channel to form new waterways. The breaks are often along paths worn down by hippos, and the water then rapidly flows down along the newfound courses into the surrounding, lower-lying floodplains. Large channels are thus diverted into new ones, and the diversions may radically change the pattern and distribution of flow in the Delta.[14]

Clean waters

One feature characterizes the waters of the Okavango more than any other: its overall purity and clarity. Few other large rivers in the world boast such cleanliness, but the good quality of Okavango water is both an asset and a constraint. On the plus side, the water is so

Most river beds are lined with Kalahari sand, the sand usually forming a rather even carpet. In some places, however, the sand is shaped into underwater dunes called mega-ripples (left). *The waters of the Okavango are very clean, such as here in the Cuebe River* (right).

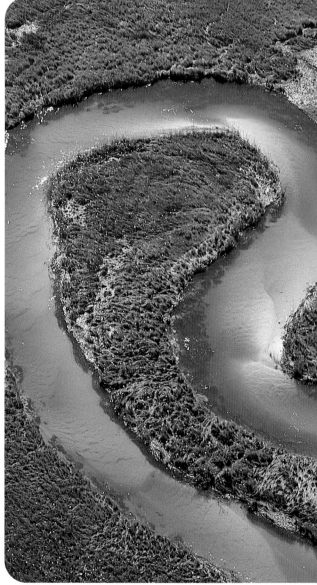

clean because there are few sources of pollution or contamination. Soils in its catchment and along its riverbanks also do not erode easily and the water is thus free of the muddiness that colours most other rivers during the rainy season. Unlike lake water in most hot and arid parts of the world, water in the Delta is surprisingly free of salts, an aspect described on page 90. All of this means that rural people can drink and wash in the water with less risk of picking up diseases than in dirtier rivers.

The purity of Okavango water also means that it is extremely deficient in nutrients, and this places a limit on life in the river. There would be more fish, birds and plant life in the river if there were more nitrogen, phosphorous and other minerals. During aerial surveys of the Angolan rivers in May 2003, we were struck by the almost complete absence of water birds. Many people assume that much of the wildlife was killed during the last few decades of hostilities in Angola. That may be true of large mammals and many birds, but it is hard to escape the conclusion that some other factor must be responsible for the absence of ducks, egrets and herons, for example. Most of the wetlands surveyed from the air were far from any human habitation and possible disturbance, and we conclude that many of those wetlands are simply deficient in nutrients.

If nutrients are so scarce in the waters of the Basin, why should there be such an abundance of life in the Delta? Several explanations help answer the question. First, and most importantly, the low levels of nutrients upstream become concentrated in the Delta where the river comes to an end. An estimated 490,000 tonnes of dissolved material washes down the river each year. This is not much in relation to the volume of river water and most of the chemicals are toxic salts and other solutes of little value to plants. But there are also substantial quantities of nutrients that are trapped in the Delta, year after year. In essence, the Delta is a nutrient sink.

Second, large quantities of nutrients are released from accumulations of peat when it burns, an effect that has immediate benefit for grasslands that grow on burnt areas. Third, considerable amounts of nitrogen and phosphorous are deposited from the atmosphere, especially during anti-cyclonic weather conditions in winter. For example, about 250,000 tonnes of atmospheric deposits may land on the Delta each year, including about four kilograms of nitrogen per hectare.[15] Finally, limited quantities of nutrients are transported from the surrounding woodlands into the water in the form of dung, especially that of hippos.

In addition to dissolved chemicals now concentrated in the Delta, two other kinds of sediment inputs have helped build the fan of alluvial deposits. The first consists of the fine sand particles that settle and raise the level of the Delta's channels. Most sand is carried down from the catchment during the late summer floods when water flow is fast enough to move sand grains along. At other times, much of the sand remains trapped on the riverbed, often forming spectacular underwater dunes or mega-ripples. The second kind of sediment is suspended mud, mostly fine silt and tiny particles of plant material. However, the roughly 30,000 tonnes of these sediments that make their way down the river each year is so little that the Okavango's waters remain clear.

Key points

- The Okavango Delta is the largest wetland in southern Africa, and one of the most pristine wetlands in the world.
- The Okavango and its many tributaries arise in Angola. All water flowing down to the Delta thus comes from the Angolan catchment.
- Of all water flowing into the Delta, 45% comes down the Cuito and 55% along the Cubango/ Okavango River. The Cuito delivers more water between June and December than the Cubango/ Okavango.
- Much of the north-western drainage consists of rivers that flow quite rapidly along a single channel with a moderately steep gradient. Rivers in the eastern catchment, by contrast, meander along very shallow, broad valleys.
- Frequent changes to the distribution of water and habitats in the Delta are due to the deposition of sand in the channels and resulting switches in the direction of water flow.
- The river and Delta water is exceptionally clean and clear because few minerals or clay particles are released from the Kalahari sands and because floodplain and marshes along the rivers filter out nutrients and mud particles.
- Mineral nutrients and sediments that do make their way down the river eventually collect in the Delta, making the Delta biologically productive.
- Total volumes of water flowing into the Delta average 9.4 cubic kilometres per year, but there are wide year-to-year fluctuations as a result of variations in rainfall in Angola.
- The extent of flooding in the Delta each year depends on inflow from Angola, the degree of flooding in the previous year, rainfall over the Delta and evaporation rates.

6
LIVING RESOURCES

The Okavango's plants
and animals

The Okavango's natural resources offer
many benefits, such as reeds to build walls
and the pleasure of beauty and tranquility.

THE RIVER is at the heart and core of the Okavango Basin, and a variety of aquatic plants and animals live in and make good use of the river water. Surrounding the river is another community of organisms, those that normally live in the dry woodlands growing on the vast area of Kalahari sand across which the river flows. The mix and interface of life along the river – where sand meets water and aquatic and terrestrial organisms come together – is thus rich and varied.

The blend between aquatic and terrestrial life varies a good deal, however, because the Basin covers a wide spectrum of environmental conditions that have a major impact on the nature of living organisms. In the northern catchment, the rivers are narrow lines that carve their way through large expanses of woodland. Higher rainfall up here means that the woodlands are evergreen and semi-tropical. Further south, the rivers are wider, often with broad margins of floodplains beyond which there are drier, deciduous woodlands. A variety of organisms are specialized inhabitants of the floodplains, and these become more prominent in the Delta where there are more nutrients and swamps, and seasonally inundated habitats predominate. Most soils

around the Delta were formed during more extensive flooding in wetter times, and these soils support different vegetation communities that add yet another component to the Basin's natural wealth. It is all these dimensions and components that contribute to the diversity of the river system and that affect the lives of people in determining what resources are available for their use.

Fish and fishing

People who came to settle along the Okavango's waterways must have found fish a welcome part of their diet. Fish remain a significant feature in the lives of many people today who fish for food or earn incomes by selling their catches or providing fishing trips for tourists. To our knowledge, no systematic surveys of fish have been done in the Angolan catchment, but many species found there also occur downstream in Kavango and Ngamiland where a total of 83 species has been identified.[1]

Despite there being over 80 species in the Basin, any one stretch of the river or area of the Delta is usually occupied by only 15 to 30 species, and these are

Bream (below) are prized catches for recreational fishermen, who use much more sophisticated gear than the home-made rod used by a man at the confluence of the Cuito and Cubango/Okavango (right).

normally dominated by four or five species that out-number or outweigh all the others. Fish communities are broadly divided along two dimensions. First, food preferences and specializations separate different species into detritivores that eat tiny food particles in the water, herbivores that feed on plant material, and predators of other fish. A second level divides them into habitats, with different fish preferring the mainstream, rocky areas and rapids, backwaters, permanent swamps and the floodplains.

Of the various habitats, the floodplains and seasonal swamps are of greatest value as places in which most fish breed. Flooding starts when the rising river and channel waters push out over flat surrounding ground, and the biggest floodplains form in years when river levels are highest (see photographs on page 84). The most important feature of the flooded areas is that they are rich in nutrients, which, together with the water, allow a lush growth of plants and the emergence of insects and other small animals. All these organisms provide young fish with a plentiful supply of food. The floodplains also offer the young fish refuge from larger, predatory species, and the greatest survival of young fish and overall increase in fish populations occurs in years when water levels are high and flooding lasts longest. A key point is that the annual flooding of the rivers is the main driving force for the breeding of fish in the Basin.

As the floodwaters drop young fish leave the floodplains to live the remainder of their lives in the main streams or permanent backwater pools and channels. And as the floodplain dries up aquatic plants die off and nutrients from the decaying plants return to the soil. Sometimes, however, large numbers of fish are trapped in pools when the water drops, and many birds, people and other predators then enjoy a feast of helpless fish.

The Botswana government has actively promoted commercial fishing in the Delta, in part by subsidizing motorboats.

Fish populations in the Basin are much smaller than in many other freshwater systems. This is primarily because of the river water's low level of nutrients, which means that there are few algae and planktonic plants that would normally provide an abundance of food for fish in richer waters. Fish biomass is extremely variable from one habitat to another, but an average of about 120 kilograms of fish per hectare is probably a reasonable estimate of fish stocks in Kavango, while much of the Delta supports an average of between 100 and 200 kilograms of fish per hectare. Fish stocks in many other river systems and floodplains are two to four times higher.[2]

Information on fishing in Angola is not available, but large numbers of fish are harvested in Kavango and Ngamiland. However, fishing is a secondary activity for most people in these areas, contributing little to the overall cash or in-kind incomes of the majority of rural homes. Most people also pay much less attention to fishing than to farming and business activities. Three surveys in Kavango estimated that between 32 and 47% of households along the river have family members catching fish. This amounts to 6,000–9,000 households but it does not mean that people from all these homes fish every day. Two of the surveys estimated the total weight of fish caught per year in Kavango as 840 and 1,045 tonnes. Taking these figures and the number of households that catch fish into account, each person along the river consumes an average of 10–20 kilograms of fish per year.[3]

Fish are also traded in Kavango. About 42% of rural households along the river reported selling fish in one survey, and 29% stated that they bought fish rather than catching them.[4]

In the Delta about 3,200 people are reported to fish, 99% of whom are small-scale fishermen who catch food for domestic consumption. The highest concentration of fishermen is in the Panhandle because access to permanent water is much easier than elsewhere where most settlements are further from fishing grounds. The total weight of fish caught per year in the Delta probably does not exceed 400 tonnes per year: 270 tonnes by subsistence fishing and 130 tonnes by commercial fishermen.[5]

Fishing activities have changed a good deal over the years in Botswana. One change has been the disappearance of fishing from Lake Xau, the Boteti River, the Mopipi Dam and Lake Ngami. These wetlands had productive fisheries when filled with water, but they have been dry for much of the time in recent decades. Another change has been the development of commercial fisheries. One share of these is recreational fishing, which adds considerable value to the overall appeal of the Delta in attracting so many tourists and, therefore, contributing to income generated by tourism for Botswana (see page 120). Tiger fish and bream are the main species sought by recreational fishermen.

The other component to commercialization of the Delta's fish stocks is the sale of salted or frozen fish products. The Botswana government vigorously promoted these ventures

Although fish often fill mekoro boats (below left) *and fish eagles are a common sight* (below right), *fish stocks in the Okavango are much lower than in most other wetlands.*

Fish traps strung across the Cutato River just above its confluence with the Cubango River.

through the provision of financial assistance. Most funds went towards the purchase of modern fishing gear (gill nets and motor boats) and training in methods of fishing, storage and marketing. However, these efforts have largely failed and the commercial fishing sector has generally collapsed, mainly because market demands for fish are just too small. Only about 41 people remained as commercial fishermen in 2002, mainly harvesting bream species.[6]

September to December – when the river is at its lowest and fish are most concentrated – are the peak months for fishing in Kavango and the Delta. The kinds of traps or gear used to catch fish can be separated into traditional and modern methods. The most widely used traditional gear are fish funnels and kraal or corral traps, while other methods include fish fences with valved traps and corrals, scoop baskets, push baskets, bows and arrows, set fish hooks, and spears. Modern gear consists of gill and seine nets, line and hooks, wire mesh fykes and mosquito nets. In the Delta, 46% of people fish with line and hooks, 42% with baskets, 14% with gill nets, 9% with spears and 6% with traps.[7]

Fish stocks in the Delta are generally agreed to be in good health, and populations may have increased following the drop in commercial fishing. The number

of people catching fish is less than half the total in Kavango, and large areas of the Delta are simply not accessible to fishermen. By contrast, there is wide agreement that fish populations have dropped over the past 20 years in Kavango, probably as a result of the widespread use of gill and mosquito nets and growing number of people catching fish. This seems logical and reasonable, but it is also likely that the succession of years with relatively low flows over the past two decades (see page 86) has had a substantial effect on fish numbers. With smaller floods and floodplains remaining inundated for shorter periods, fewer fish would have produced eggs and the survival rates of fish fry would have been reduced. This kind of relationship between fish yields and flood levels has been established in many African wetlands[8], but more research is needed to understand the effects of human fishing pressures and patterns of flooding on fish populations in the Okavango.

A diversity of plants

There are two broad categories of plant communities in the Basin: aquatic plants associated with the river water and valleys, and terrestrial communities that surround and are independent of the river system. The composition and growth of aquatic plants varies in relation to features of water flow, flooding and nutrient levels. Plants are generally unable to establish themselves in the main stream of the river where the flow is strongest. Tall reeds and papyrus can grow in deep water while grasses and sedges are only found in shallow fringe zones that are flooded sporadically. Reeds and papyrus also grow tall in deep water because they have first and best access to nutrients carried down the main channel, whereas the growth of plants further back from this supply of nutrients is less vigorous.

Two factors have an over-riding effect on terrestrial plants: soil characteristics and rainfall. Most of the Basin is covered by Kalahari sand on which several typical species grow abundantly. They dominate the sands and form plant communities quite different from those on lower-lying, more clayey soils that often contain more nutrients and retain more water than does sand. The tallest, densest growth of vegetation is in the north of the catchment **(Figure 28)** where rainfall is highest. However, the effect of rain also means that plant production differs greatly from year to year in accordance with varying rainfall. The effect is stronger on grasses than trees, as trees produce new leaves and growth more independently of rainfall. As a result, the availability of fresh

pastures for livestock is more variable in the south than in the north because rainfall is more erratic in the southern Basin (see page 64). The high levels of production in the Delta also make clear the importance of water and nutrients for plant growth, especially in showing the concentrated plant production in the Panhandle and permanent swamps. This is where most nutrients coming down the river are extracted and used by the dense stands of papyrus. However, growth also varies from one year to the next in these wetlands.

Plant communities shape the Delta in two important ways. Dense margins of papyrus confine sand sediments to the channels (bottom), *while plant transpiration leads to dissolved salts and other chemicals being concentrated in the soils beneath the Delta (see page 90). Plants also shape the livelihoods of people, for example by providing oil and alcohol from the fruit of mangetti trees* (inset).

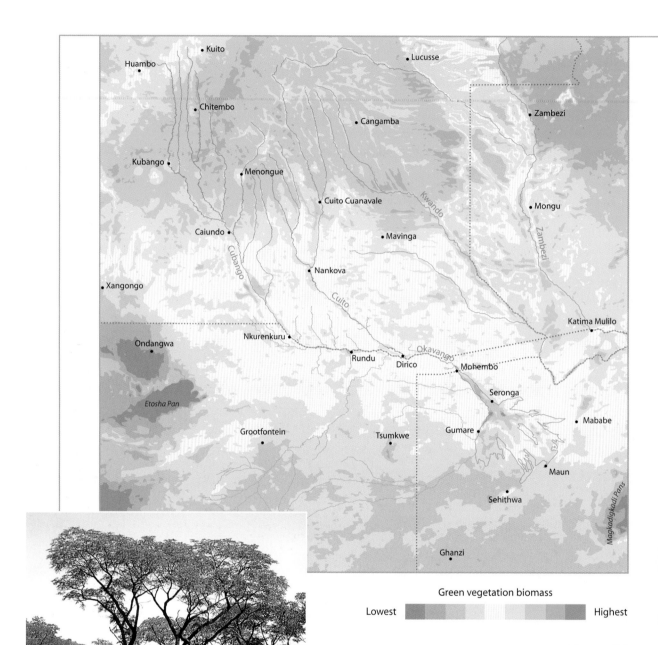

Green vegetation biomass

Lowest ▢▢▢▢▢▢▢▢ Highest

Figure 28

Plant growth is greatest where there is water and nutrients, as in the north (where rainfall is highest) and in the Delta (where plants thrive on water and nutrients supplied by the river). The large map (above) shows average plant growth over 16 seasons between 1985/1986 and 2002/2003, and also reveals the effects of degradation caused by clearing of land, for example around Menongue, Chitembo, Kubango and to the south of the Angola/Namibia border between Xangongo and Ondangwa. The eight small maps (opposite) provide measures of total plant production in each season over the past eight years, and show how growth was high in some years (2001/02 and 2002/03) but poor in others (2000/01).[9]

Woodlands on Kalahari sands in the southern half of the Basin are dominated by Burkea africana, *also known as wild syringa.*

1995/96

Kubango •
• Menongue
Rundu
• Mohembo
• Maun

1999/00

Kubango •
• Menongue
Rundu
• Mohembo
• Maun

1996/97

Kubango •
• Menongue
Rundu
• Mohembo
• Maun

2000/01

Kubango •
• Menongue
Rundu
• Mohembo
• Maun

1997/98

Kubango •
• Menongue
Rundu
• Mohembo
• Maun

2001/02

Kubango •
• Menongue
Rundu
• Mohembo
• Maun

1998/99

Kubango •
• Menongue
Rundu
• Mohembo
• Maun

2002/03

Kubango •
• Menongue
Rundu
• Mohembo
• Maun

*A magnificent baobab
is reflected in the
waters of the Delta*

Twelve different types of vegetation have been recognized and described here **(Figure 29)**. The first five cover very large areas because they are largely associated with the expansive Kalahari sands. The next three units are formed by the network of rivers that drain the Basin, while the remaining four vegetation types are associated with the Delta as it is now or with previous patterns of flooding in that area. All the vegetation types are really broad mosaics of many different sub-units that are too small and complex to map and describe here.

The highest rainfall and elevations provide the basis of the *Planalto Grasslands* in the most northerly part of the Basin. As the name suggests, trees and other woody plants are not abundant, the whole area being characterized by extensive grasslands. *Loudetia simplex* is the commonest grass species. Much of the unit consists of thousands of small streams surrounded by swampy sponges from which water seeps into the headwaters of the Cubango, Cutato and Cuchi rivers. Black peat soils lie beneath the sponges, while the surrounding

Figure 29

Vegetation types are broadly divided into five units associated with Kalahari sands, three types along the network of rivers, and four units in and around the Delta. Differences in vegetation on the Kalahari sands are mainly due to changing rainfall, while differences in the rivers and Delta are largely dependent on depth and duration of flooding.[10]

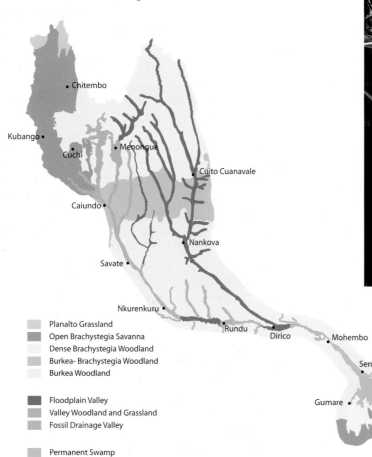

Planalto Grassland
Open Brachystegia Savanna
Dense Brachystegia Woodland
Burkea- Brachystegia Woodland
Burkea Woodland

Floodplain Valley
Valley Woodland and Grassland
Fossil Drainage Valley

Permanent Swamp
Seasonal Swamp
Mopane Woodland
Acacia Woodland

Water lilies add colour to quiet backwaters.

grassland, perhaps remnant floodplains from wetter periods, punctuate the carpet of woodland in places. Average rainfall exceeds 900 millimetres per year, while the band of *Burkea-Brachystegia Woodlands* to the south receives average falls of 700 to 900 millimetres. This is a transition zone between the evergreen *Brachystegia* forests to the north and drier, deciduous woodlands to the south. As one moves further south, increasing numbers of *Burkea africana*, *Pterocarpus angolensis*, *Baikiaea plurijuga*, *Schinziophyton rautanenii*, *Guibourtia coleosperma* and *Terminalia sericea* trees are present. These are the species that characterize *Burkea Woodlands* all the way south to the northern limits of the Delta.

Only the larger river valleys are shown in **Figure 29**, but the accounts that follow hold true for the many other river valleys. In the western half of the catchment and along the whole Cubango/Okavango, the vegetation is typically a mix of woodlands, grasslands and floodplain grasses, sedges and reeds termed *Valley Woodlands and Grasslands*. Some sections of the main rivers in the north-western catchment filter through dense *Phragmites* reed beds (see page 78). True riverine forest is rare, but sections of the Cubango north of Caiundu carry dense fringes of *Syzygium* forest, while there is an unusual pocket of dense woodland on the sandy islands near Andara. Much of the natural vegetation in this unit has been cleared along the southern banks of the river in Kavango (page 147). The *Floodplain Valleys* of the eastern catchment are characteristically open areas. Reed beds in the centre of the valleys are bordered by wide margins of seasonally flooded grassland. Beyond the wet grasslands is another zone of drier grassland that is flooded only sporadically. There are very few woody plants on these floodplains. Several *Fossil Drainage Valleys* have been demarcated in **Figure 29**. None of these carry water but their vegetation is quite different from the surrounding woodlands on sandy soils. This is because most of the valley soils are more clayey calcisols. The bottoms of the valleys are often open grasslands with copses of *Acacia* and *Terminalia* thickets.

There are four major vegetation units in and around the Delta. In the centre where water levels are deepest and water is present year-round are the *Permanent Swamps*. Papyrus *Cyperus papyrus* dominates the deepest waters and forms margins to the major channels. Water seeps through the walls of papyrus into the back swamp, but sandy sediments are confined to the channels. These are flanked by reed beds of *Phragmites* and *Typha* bulrushes and then *Miscanthus junceus* in the shallowest waters. Floodwaters usually reach the *Seasonal Swamps* during the dry winter months (see page 85), although heavy falls of rain may cause local flooding in summer. The diverse zones of vegetation in the *Seasonal Swamps* vary according to depth and duration of flooding.

Dense forests of waterberry trees (Syzygium guineense) *line the banks of the Cubango River near the town of Kubango.*

grasslands are mainly on Kalahari sand. Similar spongy swamps are also abundant in *Open Brachystegia Savanna*, a unit that is based mainly on ferrasol soils. Its species composition is similar to the next unit, but it is characterized by more open areas of grassland and extensive clearings for crops.

Dense *Brachystegia Woodlands* stretch across the whole northern quarter of the Basin. Dominant trees include several *Brachystegia* species, *Julbernadia paniculata*, *Pteleopsis anisoptera* and *Cryptosepalum pseudotaxus*. Small areas of

Short grasslands, mainly of *Imperata cylindrica*, dominate patches that are seldom flooded while various sedges are abundant in areas flooded more often. Many thousands of islands of different sizes are dotted across both the *Permanent* and *Seasonal Swamps*. All have a clearly defined tree line marking the highest floodwater levels. The islands harbour a variety of trees and palms which add considerable diversity to the Delta and play an important role in concentrating salts (see page 90).

Surrounding the Delta are two broad areas of woodland: *Mopane Woodlands* to the north-east, and *Acacia Woodlands* to the south-west. Both vegetation types are on soils formed by flooding during much wetter periods, perhaps tens of thousands of years ago (see page 35). The dominant species in the first unit is

Colophospermum mopane, while *Acacia erioloba* and *A. tortilis* characterize the south-western area. *Terminalia sericea* and *Philenoptera nelsii* are abundant in both areas. Soils in the north-east appear more clayey, and thus hold more water, than in the south-west where the ground is more sandy. This may be why *Colophospermum mopane* is common in the north-east.

Autumn colours of deciduous Burkea Woodland *in the south* (below) *differ from the solid carpet of* Dense Brachystegia Woodland *in the north of the Basin* (opposite below). *Rich communities of plants and animals are hidden beneath the surface of the water* (right). *For example, there are at least 27 snail species, six crustaceans and over 200 species of aquatic insects, all playing important roles in the cycling of nutrients and biological production of the Okavango.*

The sharp line marks the Southern Buffalo Fence north of Lake Ngami and Toteng. Colour differences on either side of the fence are due to a change in vegetation structure and/or species composition caused by differences in grazing pressure. One possibility is that overgrazing has occurred north of the line because of wildlife being concentrated by the fence in this area of good grazing. South of the fence, cattle numbers and grazing pressure declined as a result of the cattle cull following the 1995 outbreak of lung sickness (see page 150).

The sandy islands near Andara are unlike any others anywhere on the river. The tall, dense growth of trees remains intact, partly because some of the islands have been used as burial grounds for Mbukushu leaders. Several unusual plant species occur there and every effort should be made to conserve this diverse community of plants.

The many uses of plants

Plant life provides people in the Basin with many different benefits. Most uses are for domestic purposes and for the immediate benefit of households, but plant products are also sold to earn cash incomes, and many goods are exported from the region. Of the different products, wood is much the most important because most homes are built largely of timber harvested from local trees, and the great majority of households use wood as a fuel. Most fuel wood is collected from dead trees. Wood is also converted to charcoal and sold in many Angolan villages. Charcoal is not produced in Kavango or Ngamiland, but the sale of firewood alongside roads in Kavango has increased greatly over the past five years. Sleds and dug-out boats *(mekoros)* are also made from pieces of wood or tree trunks. Other major uses of wood are for fences, furniture and craft production. There is no large-scale commercial logging of trees in the Basin.

A large variety of trees and shrubs produce nuts and fruits that are consumed. For example, a recent survey found that nuts and fruits from between 35 and 50 different species were eaten in any one area in Kavango.[11] Most of these are taken only occasionally but others provide relatively large quantities of food. Mangetti *(Schinziophyton rautanenii)* nuts are used on a large scale to brew an alcoholic drink, *kashipembe*,

and as a source of oil. The potential for producing distilled and bottled liqueur and oil for the international cosmetics industry is now being explored. The leaves of different wild spinach plants are consumed, as are water lilies and various mushrooms. Many plants are used for medicinal purposes, and the same recent study on plant uses found that the healing properties of between 20 and 40 different species were used in any one area.

Grass is used mainly for grazing the many cattle in the Basin, and some of the most heavily stocked areas (see page 153) are badly overgrazed. Most rural houses are thatched with grass and/or reeds, while reeds are used extensively to make sleeping mats, walls, palisades and fences. Kavango has recently seen the development of a substantial export industry of thatching grass (largely *Eragrostis pallens*), much of it going to commercial thatching companies elsewhere in Namibia. The value of thatch exports probably exceeds several hundred thousand US$ per year.

There are two major centres of craft production in the Basin. One is around the Delta where there is a large and internationally renowned basket industry. Most baskets are woven from grass bound with *Hyphaene petersiana* palm leaves and then decorated with dyes from *Berchemia discolor* and *Euclea divinorum*. The great majority of the approximately 1,500 weavers are women who collectively earn about US$120,000 per year. Some weavers, however, earn much more than others. The main centres of basket production are at Etsha and Gumare. Baskets completely dominate craft production in Ngamiland unlike the other centre for craft. This is in Kavango where most articles are carved from wood, especially *Pterocarpus angolensis* and *Guibourtia coleosperma*, but mats, pottery, baskets and jewellery are also produced. The majority of articles were sold along the road between Rundu and Katjinakatji up until 10 years ago, but an increasing export trade of small items and large wooden statues has developed recently. Many of these items are sold in Windhoek and Okahandja, and beyond. Large rough blocks of wood are also exported for the use of carvers elsewhere, and the extent and effect of harvesting these large pieces needs to be investigated. The total value of craft production in Kavango is unknown.

The value of labour, wood and thatching grass invested in a roof is so substantial that it is better to move it than build another one (top). Beehives, fashioned from bark, are a common sight in Angola (centre). The trunks of teak, marula and several other large trees are used to hollow-out mekoro boats, which provide transport to harvest reeds in the Delta (below). The reeds are used to make sleeping mats, walls and fences.

Most uses of plants described so far bring value to the lives of many people. Vegetation is also burnt in winter to stimulate the growth of new pastures, clear land for cultivation or remove vegetation from waterholes. However, many fires run away accidentally, leading to huge areas being burnt year after year **(Figure 30)** and substantial damage to plant life. The burning has several effects. First, large areas of grazing are lost. For example, an average of 32% of the surface of the Kavango Region burnt each year between 1989 and 2001. Second, young trees are killed and there are almost no young trees of several valuable timber species in many areas. Third, valuable timber trees

There is no commercial craft industry in Angola. However, Angolans are well known for their traditional production of decorative items used during religious and healing rites, and some of the skills now used in Kavango and Ngamiland to produce and sell craft were probably derived from this heritage in Angola. The Angolan boy (right above) carries water from the Cuelei River on a wooden scooter, the joints of which are held in place by rifle cartridges. The presence of thousands of military vehicles over the past few decades in the Basin are recalled in the small wooden helicopters and trucks on sale in Kavango (right), while skills developed over centuries to make grass and reed mats are now used to produce beautiful baskets (below).

Figure 30

Fires are one of the most serious environmental problems in the Basin because they cause the loss of valuable woodlands and soil nutrients. Pastures are also lost, and an average of one-third of all pastures in Kavango were burnt each year between 1989 and 2001. The map shows the number of times that different places were burnt during that period in Kavango.[12]

Number of years burnt

0
1 - 2
3 - 4
5 - 6
7 - 8
9 - 13

(and other species) are destroyed. Fourth, large areas become impenetrable thickets of shrubs, especially of *Terminalia sericea* and *Baphia massaiensis*. Fifth, the loss of nitrogen and sulphur to the atmosphere and the burning of leaf litter and humus that would decompose into organic nutrients in the ground reduces soil fertility. Sixth, fierce fires may kill livestock, wildlife and people. Finally, the extent and frequency of burning means that fires in the Basin add significant volumes of ash and carbon dioxide to the atmosphere. What impact this has on global pollution remains unknown, however.

The effects of fire are most prominent in the Basin's woodlands. However, large areas of grassland and reed beds also burn every year in the Valley Marshlands and Floodplain Valleys in Angola and in the Delta's Permanent Swamps and Seasonal Swamps (see page 77), where grazing and reeds used for domestic construction are lost. Some of the fires ignite peat, the mass of decayed and decaying plant material that has accumulated over decades beneath the swamp vegetation. The layers of peat can be several metres thick and peat fires may smoulder for years (see page 87). The fires cause concentrations of nutrients to be released from the peat and these nourish the growth of rich grasslands once the fires die off.

Wild, wildlife

'Okavango' conjures up two images for many people: one a vast area of swamps and the other an abundance of wildlife. These are the main qualities that make the Delta so attractive to tourists and famous around the world. 'Wildlife' generally includes all those large mammals for which Africa is well known: elephants, lions, antelope, crocodiles and so many other spectacular animals. The aerial surveys to count and map the distributions of large species show that there are indeed large numbers of wildlife in the Delta and also to the north-east in the area extending up to the Kwando River and Linyanti Swamps. For example, eight surveys over the past 10 years have produced estimated populations of between 160,000 and 260,000 large mammals in the Delta.[13] The highest numbers were during dry season counts when many

The great abundance of antelope and buffalo in the Delta provides large predators with food. As a result, there are relatively high numbers of lions (right)*, spotted hyaenas and jackals* (below)*, cheetah* (opposite)*, wild dogs and leopards.*

animals are concentrated near the water. Few other places in Africa – indeed the world – offer such a concentration of wildlife. Why should there be such abundance here? First, very few people live in this area (see page 127), and so animals have not suffered from hunting that normally occurs wherever people live near wildlife. Second, wildlife in the Delta has benefited from protection, especially in the form of the Moremi Game Reserve, strictly controlled hunting quotas and the promotion of practices that allow those people living in the Delta to benefit from wildlife (see page 166). Third, alluvial soils in the area are richer in nutrients than in many other areas, especially the poor Kalahari sands. The nutrients are of immediate benefit to plants, particularly grasses, which provide good grazing. Fourth, drinking water is available at permanent sources in the various rivers and swamps and in temporary pans that fill during the rains. Fifth, the whole area offers a diverse range of habitats, enabling certain species to specialize on the grasslands, others to thrive on woodlands, and yet others on the swamps and floodplains. In addition, the diversity of habitats provides other more generalist species with different sources of food in different seasons.

The wealth of wildlife in and around the Delta stands in great contrast to the small numbers elsewhere in the Basin **(Figure 31)**. The only area in Kavango with reasonable numbers of wildlife is the Mahango Game Reserve, a tiny area of 250 square kilometers, which is home to about 2,000 large mammals.[14] Elsewhere in the remaining densely settled area of Kavango just a few hippos and crocodiles remain along the river. Few large mammals apparently exist in the large Angolan section of the Basin, a conclusion based on three observations. Firstly, much of the area consists of woodlands growing on Kalahari sands, which generally support little wildlife. Large areas in the north-west, where soils are richer in nutrients, have been cleared by the many people living there. Second, we are not aware of any reports of large numbers of wildlife in the Angolan Basin area. Thirdly, during an aerial survey over 2,600 kilometres in May 2003 and covering representative zones in the catchment we saw fewer than 30 large mammals. We were also struck by the absence in most areas of trails or paths normally worn into the floodplain vegetation alongside the rivers. The only area in which some footpaths were seen was in the northern headwaters of the Cuito and Cuanavale rivers. In addition, very few large water birds (such as ducks and herons) were seen. Taking these observations together with the low concentrations of nutrients in river water (see page 92) and soils along the rivers (see page 42) suggests that most of the Angolan catchment does not provide a habitat suited to large numbers of wildlife. It is also probable that soldiers killed many elephant, buffalo, hippo and other large species during the recent strife.

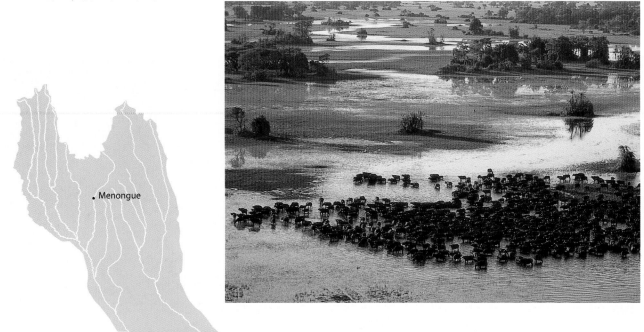

Wildlife biomass

- None
- Low
- Medium
- High
- Unknown
- Protected area

Figure 31

The greatest concentrations of wildlife or large mammals, such as the buffalo above, are in the Delta and in Mahango Game Reserve in Kavango. There are no large mammals along most of the southern bank of the river in Kavango. Although no systematic surveys of wildlife have been done, it is likely that densities of large mammals are very low in Angola.

Lechwe are most abundant in and around the permanent swamps of the Delta. Total numbers are estimated to be between 50,000 and 60,000, making them the most abundant large mammals in the Delta. Populations increased greatly up until the mid 1980s but then declined, perhaps in response to lower levels of flooding. Some lechwe occur along rivers in the eastern catchment in Angola.

Lechwe

- None
- Low
- High
- Unknown

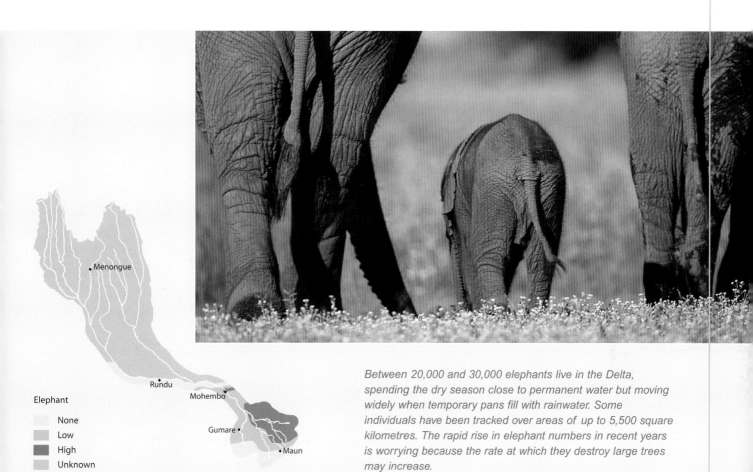

Elephant

None
Low
High
Unknown

Between 20,000 and 30,000 elephants live in the Delta, spending the dry season close to permanent water but moving widely when temporary pans fill with rainwater. Some individuals have been tracked over areas of up to 5,500 square kilometres. The rapid rise in elephant numbers in recent years is worrying because the rate at which they destroy large trees may increase.

Tsessebe

None
Low
High
Unknown

Tsessebe are usually seen grazing on open grasslands that are flooded periodically. There are over 5,000 in the Delta, a number that has apparently declined from an estimated population of about 10,000 a decade ago.

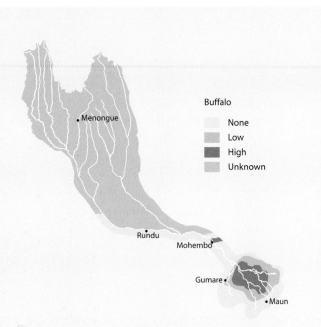

Buffalo

None
Low
High
Unknown

Buffalo are usually closely associated with permanent water and herds of several hundred buffalo are sometimes seen grazing on the Delta's floodplains. A total of between 30,000 and 40,000 buffalo occur in the Delta, while approximately 500 live in the Mahango Game Reserve.

There are perhaps several thousand hippos in the Delta and another 200 or so in the Mahango Game Reserve. In both areas they are strictly confined to areas of open water from where they venture short distances to feed at night. Hippo paths through the swamps allow water to switch direction and to form new channels (see page 91).

Hippo

None
Present
Unknown

Giraffe

None
Present
Unknown

There are usually between 5,000 and 7,000 giraffe in the Delta. Small herds are generally seen in their preferred woodland habitat in and around seasonal swamps in the eastern and southern parts of the Delta.

The majority of approximately 20,000 impala occur around the eastern and southern areas of seasonal swamps in the Delta. Small herds of impala are usually encountered in woodlands, the habitat they prefer as browsers.

Impala

None
Present
Unknown

Sitatunga
None
Present
Unknown

Sitatunga are confined to permanent swamps in the Delta. Populations of these small antelope have declined significantly over the past 15 years, one possible cause being the reduced levels of flooding due to lower inflows from the Okavango River (see page 86).

Reedbuck, like lechwe, tsessebe and sitatunga, prefer the permanent wetlands in the centre of the Delta, along the Panhandle and in the Mahango Game Reserve. Small numbers are probably present along many of the larger rivers in the eastern part of the Angolan catchment.

Reedbuck
None
Present
Unknown

Waterbuck

None
Present
Unknown

Waterbuck are now extinct in the Mahango Game Reserve, while a population of several hundred remains in the Delta. Although these antelope are closely linked to permanent water, they are often found in surrounding grasslands.

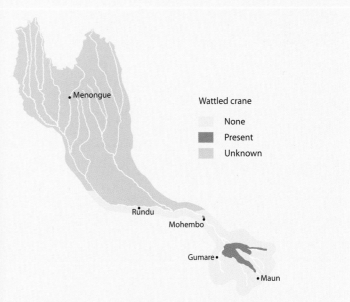

Wattled crane

None
Present
Unknown

The population of approximately 1,300 wattled cranes in the Delta represents over 15% of all these rare and majestic birds south of the equator in Africa. Most are concentrated in the permanent swamps in the centre of the Delta where their main breeding season starts in August.

Over 500 species of birds have been recorded in the Delta, and about 420 species in the tiny Mahango Game Reserve, making both areas magnets for birdwatchers. More importantly, the wetlands provide a home for substantial populations of many birds that are uncommon elsewhere. These are three of the Okavango's 'specials': the African skimmer (above), *Pel's fishing owl* (centre) *and saddlebilled stork* (bottom).

The value of tourism

Discussing tourism in a chapter about plants and animals may seem odd, but there is a close and mutually beneficial linkage between them. It is the natural resources of the region that draw so many people to the Okavango from around the world. In turn, plants and animals gain value and protection because they are important to visitors and thus to the enterprises and governments that earn money from tourism. There is a clear and increasing concentration of tourism as one moves downstream towards the Delta **(Figure 32)**, especially downstream of Divundu.

To some degree, the spread mirrors the increasing accumulation of nutrients in the Delta (see page 93). And this is not coincidental, because it is the concentration of nutrients that enables the Delta to host such a variety of rich habitats, plant communities and wildlife. The other reason is that the Namibian and Botswana governments have set aside areas to protect wildlife and promote tourism. There are very few, if any, tourists to the Angolan catchment area, where the only hotel in Menongue caters largely for business visitors. Most visitors to hotels in Rundu are also on business, whereas most guests at hotels, lodges and camps downstream from Rundu are tourists.

The majority of tourists to the Basin are from outside Africa. Between 1999 and 2001, for example, 39% of visitors to Moremi Game Reserve were from Europe, 17% from South Africa, 16% from Botswana, 11% from South America, 7%

from North America, and 9% from elsewhere.[15] Visitors to Popa Game Park between 1998 and 2002 were categorized into Namibians (22%), South Africans (24%) and elsewhere in the world (54%). The number of tourists has grown astronomically over the past four decades. Almost no one visited the area in the 1960s but now more than 50,000 people come to the Delta each year. Reliable statistics are not available for Kavango, but over 15,000 tourists probably visit the region annually.

Most resorts provide accommodation of the highest quality, each room often tucked away in its own piece of unspoiled Okavango.

Figure 32
There is only one hotel in the Basin in Angola that might cater for tourists, whereas there are 19 hotels, lodges and camps in Kavango and about 50 accommodation facilities in and around the Delta.

▲ Hotel, lodge or safari camp
Panhandle
Permanent Swamp
Seasonal Swamp
Protected area

Many animals are now accustomed to people in vehicles, and few places in the world offer opportunities to see lions as close as this.

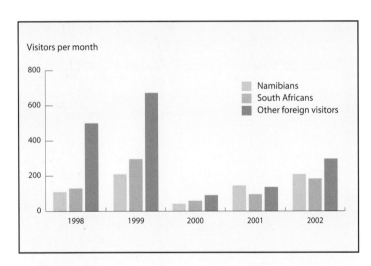

Figure 33

In accordance with increasing tourism to the Basin over the past three decades, the number of visitors to Popa Game Park from South Africa and elsewhere rose by 4,000 people between 1998 and 1999. Then came the unrest in 2000, when numbers of foreign tourists dropped by almost 10,000 from the 1999 total. Although the number of visitors then increased, by 2002 it was still less than half the 1999 total. Figures in the graph are the average number of visitors each month between 1998 and 2002.[16]

The growth in value and benefits from tourism has been enormous. Following diamond exports, tourism is now the second biggest earner for Botswana, contributing about 5% to the country's Gross Domestic Product in 2000. Including air travel, each foreign tourist spends an average of about US$1,000 per day during a visit to the Delta. Approximately 60% of people employed in Ngamiland are in jobs associated with tourism and infrastructure and services that support the industry.[17] Other benefits to Ngamiland have come in the form of improved transport and communications infrastructure and expanded wholesale and retail sectors. Finally, tourism to the Delta has helped put Botswana on the world map, giving it a reputation that few countries in Africa match.

Tourism is, however, a delicate business. That lesson unfolded after the spate of unrest that started in Kavango at the end of 1999 and early in 2000. Numbers of visitors plummeted **(Figure 33)** as tourism abandoned north-eastern Namibia. Many resorts and hotels in Kavango closed for a year or longer. Tourism to the Delta was also badly affected and conditions were aggravated by instability in Zimbabwe. For example, the number of visitors to Moremi Game Reserve dropped by about 35% between 1999 and 2001.

Glossina morsitans is the only species of tsetse fly found in the Delta.

Figure 34

Tsetse flies occur widely in tropical Africa from where they extend to their most southerly limits in the Delta. The biting flies transmit blood parasites called *Trypanosoma*, which affect cattle and people (as sleeping sickness). Twenty-two species of tsetse fly occur in Africa, but the only one in Ngamiland is *Glossina morsitans*. The flies disappeared when cattle and game were decimated by the rinderpest epidemic in 1896, but returned once the animal populations recovered over the next three decades. The first confirmed case of human sleeping sickness was reported in 1939 in the Delta. A variety of control methods have been used, including the killing of wildlife hosts, clearing of bush, and ground and aerial spraying with DDT and endosulphan. The application of insecticides from the air was stopped in 1992, partly in response to concerns that the chemicals caused considerable environmental damage, including the loss of fish in the Delta. Plastic sheets impregnated with synthetic ox odour and insecticide are now used to control the flies.

Key notes

- Fish stocks are generally much lower than in many other freshwater wetlands, mainly because of low nutrient levels in the Okavango. The annual flooding of the rivers is the main driving force for the breeding of fish in the Basin.
- Stocks of fish in the Delta are considered to be in good health, but those in Kavango have apparently declined, perhaps due to over-exploitation and/or lower levels of flooding.
- Aquatic vegetation varies largely in relation to strength of water flow, frequency of flooding and nutrient levels, while soil characteristics and rainfall are the most important factors to affect terrestrial plant communities.
- The main exports of plant products from the Basin are baskets, wood craft, firewood and thatching grass.
- Fires are one of the most serious environmental problems in the Basin because they result in the loss of valuable woodlands, pastures and soil nutrients.
- One of the greatest concentrations of wildlife in Africa is in and around the Delta where the number of large mammals varies between 160,000 and 260,000.
- Most tourism in the Basin is concentrated downstream of Divundu and into the Delta.
- Tourism to the Delta and Kavango has grown rapidly and earns the Basin considerable income. However, recent insecurity and instability caused the number of visitors to plummet.

7

PEOPLE

Change and motion

About half of all people around
the Okavango are children.

THE OKAVANGO BASIN has never been an easy place to be, at least in comparison to many other areas in southern Africa. Historically, all but a few people chose to live in other places that offered better agricultural potential and economic opportunities, and where human and livestock diseases were less prevalent. People in the Basin also often suffered from raids by neighbouring stronger tribes (see page 52). Their vulnerability stemmed from the very fact that tribal groups were small and thus comparatively weak. The Basin's population has indeed always been small, and even now it makes up a tiny proportion of all the citizens of Angola, Namibia and Botswana (Figure 35).

Given such difficulties, it is not surprising that the majority of the Basin's predecessors were forced to immigrate here (see page 51), and people have continued to be mobile. This is evident in the migration of people to the towns of Rundu and Maun and the massive displacement of Angolans during hostilities in recent decades, for example. Impermanence is thus one feature of the Basin's population. Another is change, and peoples' lives have altered remarkably rapidly over the past 100 years. There have been many kinds of changes, some of which have led to improved health and education due to services provided at clinics and schools. Numbers of people have grown very quickly as a result of lower child mortality rates and longer life spans. New jobs and business ventures have bought benefits to many households. These are all positive changes, but change has also been accompanied by turbulence in Angola. Some Angolans have come through the upheavals with better lives, but many others have not been as lucky.

Where do people live?

The total population of the Basin – the catchment area in Angola and within 20 kilometres of the river in Kavango and Delta in Botswana – amounts to about 600,000 people. This is the number suggested by estimates for each country in the following table, which also show that approximately 58% of all people live in the Angolan catchment, 27% in Kavango and 15% in Ngamiland.

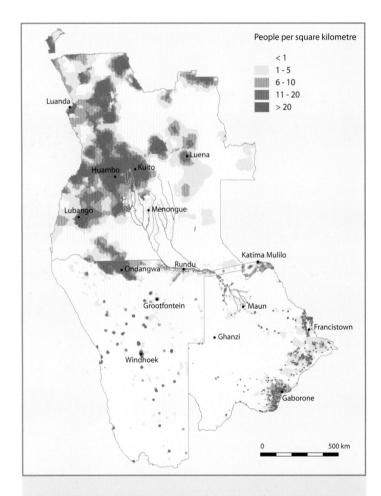

Figure 35

Most people in Angola, Namibia and Botswana live in areas far away from the Basin. Those within the Basin area of Angola make up less than 3% of the total Angolan population. Equivalent proportions for Namibia and Botswana are also small: 7% and 5%.[1] One consequence of these small percentages is that the Basin's people do not represent major political lobbies or interest groups in terms of national priorities.

The approximate number of people in the Okavango Basin				
	Rural	Urban	Total	Percent urban
Angola	300,000	50,000	350,000	14%
Kavango	121,000	42,000	163,000	26%
Ngamiland	44,000	44,000	88,000	50%
Total	465,000	136,000	601,000	23%

The totals for Ngamiland and Kavango are most accurate because they are based on national censuses held during 2001. No censuses have been conducted in recent decades in Angola and so the estimates given here are based on a variety of sources.[2] The table also gives estimates of populations in rural and urban areas, indicating that the proportion of urban residents increases across the Basin from the wettest to driest areas. Thus, only 14% of the Basin population in Angola is considered urban, compared to 26% in Kavango and 50% in Ngamiland. Again, figures for Angola are rough for reasons of poor information, but they are also approximate because urban areas in Angola are more difficult to define. We consider only Menongue and Cuito Cuanavale as urban areas, with estimated populations of 30,000 and 20,000, respectively. Many of the people rely on economic activity within these towns and many are also dependant on food aid provided by humanitarian groups. Defining urban areas is less a problem in Kavango and Ngamiland where Rundu and Maun are officially recognized as towns. It is also clear that many people in Rundu (population 42,000) and Maun (44,000) lead lives that are independent of rural livelihoods.

Most people in Angola and Ngamiland live in distinct villages, whereas households are more dispersed and strung out along the river in Kavango. A well-worn path leads from this Angolan village to its water source from the Cuatir River.

In addition to these four large towns, there are many large rural villages in which the majority of residents farm nearby. Each of these villages is home to more than 1,000 people, and the most prominent are Longa, Luassinga, Chitembo, Mumbué, Cuchi, Cutato and Kubango in Angola, Nkurenkuru, Kahenge, Ndonga, and Divundu in Kavango, and Mohembo, Nxamasere, Sepopa, Nokaneng, Seronga, Etsha, Shakawe and Gumare in Ngamiland. In addition to the concentrations of people in towns and large villages, there are high densities in the most north-western areas of the catchment and along the south bank of the river in Kavango **(Figure 36)**. This map shows the striking difference in settlement patterns across the Basin. Village structures in Angola are at least partly due to government programmes during the 1960s to control and concentrate people in villages where social services could be provided more effectively.

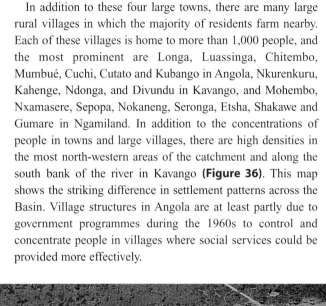

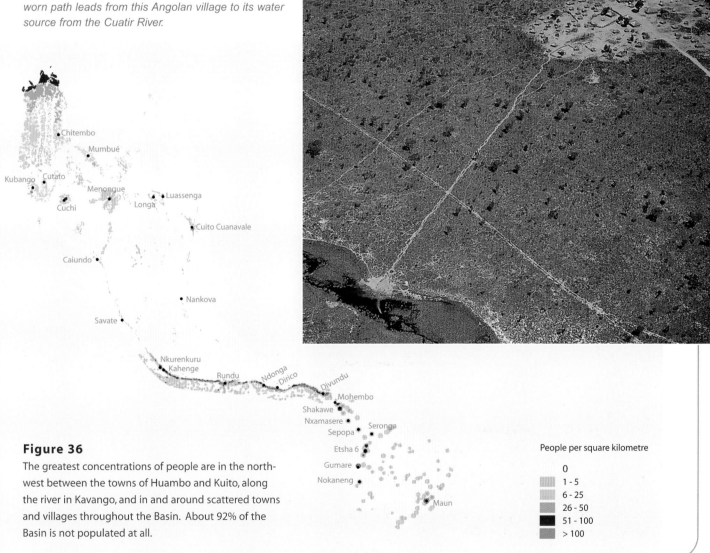

Figure 36

The greatest concentrations of people are in the north-west between the towns of Huambo and Kuito, along the river in Kavango, and in and around scattered towns and villages throughout the Basin. About 92% of the Basin is not populated at all.

People per square kilometre

	0
	1 - 5
	6 - 25
	26 - 50
	51 - 100
	> 100

Moving numbers

The total population of 600,000 has increased substantially over the past 100 years since the introduction of modern medical services, but it is only for Kavango and Ngamiland that reasonable information is available over the past 90 years **(Figure 37)**. Ngamiland had about double the population of Kavango in the early 20th century, and it continued to have a bigger population up until the early 1970s. Growth rates over those first seven decades averaged between 2% in Ngamiland and 3% in Kavango each year.

Kavango experienced very rapid growth from the early 1970s onwards, and its population soon

Where will this rural, Angolan girl move in the future?

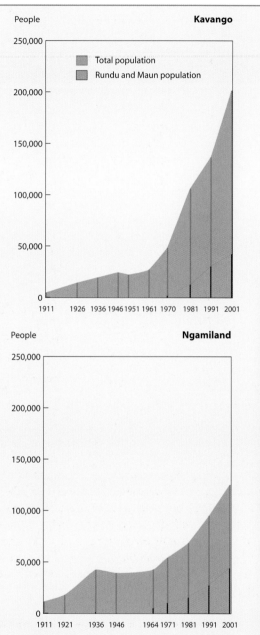

Figure 37

The number of people in Kavango and Ngamiland has grown rapidly over the past 90 years, mainly as a result of lower child mortality and longer life spans. However, rapid growth in Kavango in recent decades has mainly been due to the arrival of immigrants from Angola. Both Maun and Rundu have grown from tiny villages 40 years ago to towns with over 40,000 residents. About one in four people in the Basin area of Kavango and one in three people in Ngamiland now live in Rundu and Maun.[3]

Previously, similar numbers of people lived along the north and south banks of the river where it forms the border between Angola and Kavango. For example, surveys between 1940 and 1960 showed that populations on the northern Angolan side were slightly less than half of those in Kavango.⁴ Nowadays, however, there are probably more than 20 times more people on the southern side in Kavango, as shown so obviously by the massive areas of (pale coloured) cleared land in Kavango along this 70 kilometre stretch of river west of Rundu.

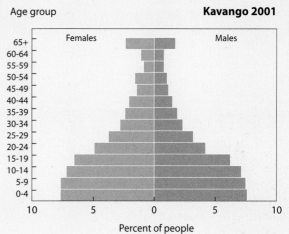

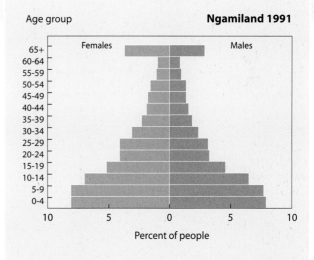

exceeded that of Ngamiland. Great numbers of people arrived in the mid-1970s during hostilities associated with Angola's independence war, and more waves of immigrants to Kavango followed other bouts of insecurity. The majority of 10,000 people who registered as refugees in Rundu between 1999 and 2002 were from Angola. However, it is also true that many people were attracted by Kavango's comparatively better economic opportunities, services and infrastructure. Such movements from Angola to Kavango may have been going on sporadically over the past few hundred years, as suggested by oral histories that relate how people moved south to escape disease and tribal wars.

The effects of recent immigration are well illustrated by the following. In 1961, Kavango's population stood at some 26,900 people. If the population had continued to increase at an annual growth rate of 3%, the total population would have been about 88,000 in 2001. However, the number of people in Kavango in 2001 was actually over 201,000. The difference of 113,000 people between these two totals was largely due to immigration. Note that 3% is the rate at which the Namibian population has grown in recent decades and it is also the rate at which the population of Ngamiland grew over the past 40 years.

Figure 38

Young people dominate the populations of Kavango and Ngamiland, with children less than 15 years making up almost half (44%) of all people. Both regions also have more females than males because more men have moved to work elsewhere in Botswana and Namibia. These age pyramids are for 2001 in Kavango and 1991 in Ngamiland. The overall shape of the pyramid for Ngamiland is unlikely to have changed since then.

Immigration from Angola is the first of four major kinds of movements by people in the Basin. The second is urbanization in which large numbers of people forsake their rural homes and economies and move to the major local towns of Maun and Rundu. The urban populations of both have grown from zero to over 40,000 people in a few decades. Annual growth for the two towns has been over 6% during the past 20 years, and the towns will double in size over the next 12 years if that rate persists. One consequence of urban growth is the rapid change in character of the population. Previously, everyone in the Basin lived a rural existence whereas urban people now make up

Visitors familiar with other parts of the Basin will be struck by the great number of children in south-eastern Angola, a consequence of high rates of fertility. Estimates of fertility in that part of Angola are not available, but they are likely to be above seven children. This is the number of live births an average woman will have during her life. Fertility rates in Kavango and Ngamiland have dropped substantially in recent years: from 6.5 in 1981 to 4.5 in 1991 in Ngamiland, and from 7.1 in 1991 to 4.2 in 2000 in Kavango.[5]

26% and 50% of the total populations in the Basin areas of Kavango and Ngamiland, respectively. The main reasons for people moving to town are to find a job or to go to school, and the populations of Maun and Rundu are therefore dominated by school-goers and young adults aged 20 to 40 **(Figure 39)**. There are also many more young women than men in the towns.

Much less is known of urbanization in Angola, but it is clear that at least the towns of Menongue and Cuito Cuanavale have expanded greatly in recent years. Other places, such as Chitembo and Caiundu, appear to have shrunk and some large villages have disappeared altogether (see page 58). Most of the changes were due to the displacement of people, the third kind of major movement by people in the Basin. Towns that grew rapidly did so because government troops forced the closure of many rural villages thought to provide support and food to UNITA. The villagers were then moved to the towns. Many people also sought refuge in towns from plundering soldiers and the continual conflict in the Basin.[6] On the other hand, UNITA brought large numbers of its supporters from the central highlands into south-eastern Angola. Much of the humanitarian work now happening in

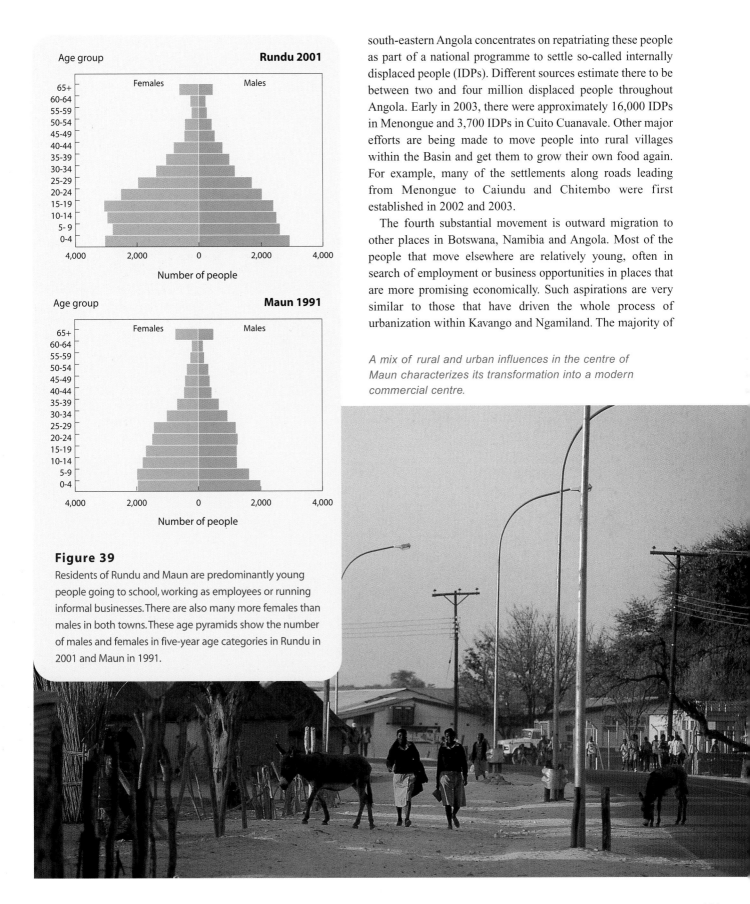

Age group   **Rundu 2001**

Females   Males

Number of people

Age group   **Maun 1991**

Females   Males

Number of people

Figure 39

Residents of Rundu and Maun are predominantly young people going to school, working as employees or running informal businesses. There are also many more females than males in both towns. These age pyramids show the number of males and females in five-year age categories in Rundu in 2001 and Maun in 1991.

south-eastern Angola concentrates on repatriating these people as part of a national programme to settle so-called internally displaced people (IDPs). Different sources estimate there to be between two and four million displaced people throughout Angola. Early in 2003, there were approximately 16,000 IDPs in Menongue and 3,700 IDPs in Cuito Cuanavale. Other major efforts are being made to move people into rural villages within the Basin and get them to grow their own food again. For example, many of the settlements along roads leading from Menongue to Caiundu and Chitembo were first established in 2002 and 2003.

The fourth substantial movement is outward migration to other places in Botswana, Namibia and Angola. Most of the people that move elsewhere are relatively young, often in search of employment or business opportunities in places that are more promising economically. Such aspirations are very similar to those that have driven the whole process of urbanization within Kavango and Ngamiland. The majority of

A mix of rural and urban influences in the centre of Maun characterizes its transformation into a modern commercial centre.

migrants to other regions are men, and the proportion of migrants has increased over the past 40 years. For example, only 4% of all people speaking a Kavango language lived outside the region in 1960, but by 1991 that figure had increased to 10%. Of all Kavango language speakers living elsewhere in Namibia in 1991, 70% were men.

Language and tribal groupings

There are fourteen major groups in the Basin that to a greater or lesser degree speak distinct languages or dialects.[7] Eleven of these are of Bantu origin and three are Khoesan languages. The broad and core distributions of the groups are shown in **Figure 40**. People have become increasingly mixed, however,

Tens of thousands of displaced people making their way home in May 2003. Ex-UNITA soldiers cross the Luassinga River on a six-week journey from Mavinga to Menongue (top), while women and children are air-lifted from Menongue to the planalto highlands in central Angola (centre). Other people walk to new villages near Mumbué (below).

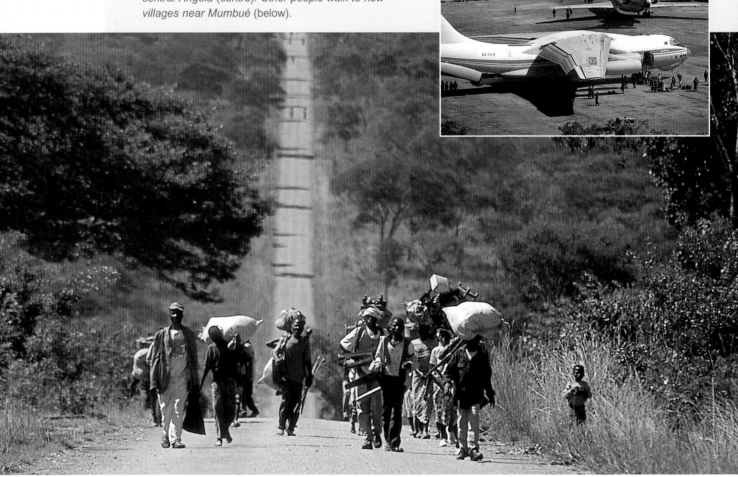

especially as a result of displacements and urbanization. The Ovimbundu people mainly live in the most north-western parts of the catchment, although UNITA relocated large numbers during the past two decades into Kuando Kubango. Ganguela and Tchokwe people dominate in most areas of the Angolan catchment, but there is a high degree of mixing, resulting in widely spaced pockets where one or the other language predominates. Many Ovimbundu, Ganguela and Tchokwe speakers also now live in Kavango, and about one-third of Rundu residents have an Angolan language as their mother tongue.

Very few !Xun San remain in Angola because they were often displaced by hostilities. Many fled from Angolan forces into Botswana in 1999. Several thousand Angolan San were also resettled in the former Bushmanland area of Namibia by the South African Defence Force in the early 1970s, and many were later taken to Schmidtsdrif in South Africa in 1989 just before Namibia's independence.

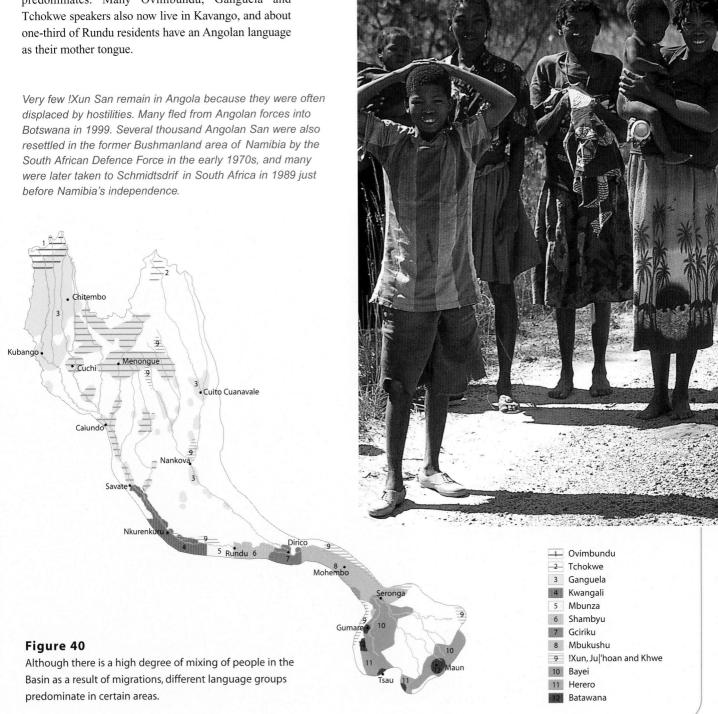

Figure 40
Although there is a high degree of mixing of people in the Basin as a result of migrations, different language groups predominate in certain areas.

1 Ovimbundu
2 Tchokwe
3 Ganguela
4 Kwangali
5 Mbunza
6 Shambyu
7 Gciriku
8 Mbukushu
9 !Xun, Ju|'hoan and Khwe
10 Bayei
11 Herero
12 Batawana

There are five distinct tribal areas along the border between Angola and Kavango. The Kwangali, who live furthest to the west, share the Rukwangali language with the Mbunza immediately to the east. They have separate tribal authorities, as do the Shambyu and Gciriku people who speak slightly different dialects of the Rumanyo language. Further east and extending down along the western margins of the Delta are the Mbukushu people. They, the Bayei, Tawana and Herero people make up the majority of residents in and around the Delta.

The small numbers of San are broadly divided into Khwe and Ju language groups. Khwe people mainly live to the east of the river in Kavango and the Delta in Ngamiland, where the ||Anikhwe and Bugahkwe sub-groups are sometimes called the River Bushmen. The Ju language group is comprised of Ju|'hoan who live on the western edges of the Delta and the dispersed, small numbers of people of !Xun in Angola. Many Khwe and !Xun people have been displaced in recent years by hostilities and political difficulties in Angola and Kavango.

Social services

Reliable information on health and education services in south-eastern Angola is not available, but it is clear that there are few health facilities and schools. The only hospital in Menongue is badly over-crowded and under-staffed. Between 7 and 10% of children die within 24 hours of being admitted to the hospital. Most of the few effective health services are run by foreign and/or non-government organizations. For Angola as a whole, the county is considered to have among the world's worst health conditions. Life expectancy is estimated to be 36 years, four years lower than the average for sub-Saharan Africa. Fifty-eight percent of people over 15 years are considered to be illiterate. About 42% of children are underweight for their age.[8] Many of the teachers in the few functional schools in the Basin have had only several years of schooling themselves. Attendance by both teachers and pupils is reportedly poor, and perhaps only 40% of children have ever been enrolled in a school.[9] In short, health and education services in the Angola present a bleak picture. What is more regrettable is the fact that whole generations have gone without these services and the majority of adults have had no schooling.

Levels of social service and development in south-eastern Angola are perhaps equivalent to those in Kavango and Ngamiland 40 years ago. These two

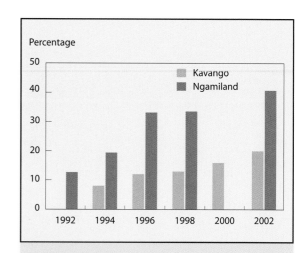

Figure 41
Namibia and Botswana share the dubious distinction of having amongst the highest rates of HIV infection in the world. The graph shows the massive increase in HIV infection, as reflected by rates of infection among pregnant women tested at hospitals in Kavango and Ngamiland between 1992 and 2002. The figures are reliable indicators of infection rates among all sexually active people, and thus about one in five such people in Kavango and one in three in Ngamiland carry HIV. Of a total population of about 250,000 people within 20 kilometres of the river and Delta (see page 126), at least 30,000 people in the two regions have HIV. Most deaths occur among people aged 25 to 40 who are often the most economically active people in the Basin, and household economies will become increasingly affected by the disease.[10]

regions now have a relatively good network of health facilities and schools, and most people have access to their services. Within 20 kilometres of the river or Delta, there are 29 clinics, eight health centres and four hospitals in Kavango, while Ngamiland has 15 health posts, six clinics and three hospitals. There are also 148 primary, 40 combined and 11 secondary schools in Kavango and 37 primary and 12 secondary schools in Ngamiland.[11] However, Kavango's schooling system is weaker than in the rest of Namibia. For example, teachers are less qualified, there are few secondary schools, buildings at many schools are in bad shape, and relatively few children complete their schooling.

Of the variety of diseases and other health problems that affect people in Basin, the most important are malaria, HIV/AIDS, acute respiratory infections, diarrhoea, scabies, tuberculosis, malnutrition and bilharzia. Most of these are directly or indirectly associated with the rural and sub-tropical environment that characterizes much of the river system. Within Kavango, malaria, acute respiratory infections, urinary bilharzia and diarrhoea infections are substantially higher in the west than in the eastern section of the river.[12] Although data on HIV/AIDS are not available for south-eastern Angola, the disease has apparently not reached the kind of epidemic level that now plagues Kavango and Ngamiland **(Figure 41)**. However, the combination of inadequate nutrition, contaminated water, poor sanitation and rapid urbanization has created environments in Angola that make the overall risk of many diseases high. This situation is compounded by a lack of health services, and the challenge of living a healthy life for Angolans is far greater than for most people in Kavango and Ngamiland. One final comparison makes the point. Out of every 1,000 live births 172 infants die on average within their first year in Angola. In Kavango, the equivalent statistic is 23 and in Ngamiland between 59 and 85 infant deaths.[13]

Diarrhoea is a major health problem in Angola, especially for young children. The disease is most prevalent in places where sanitation is poor and water is contaminated. While river water in south-eastern Angola is generally pure, the great number of people washing themselves and their clothes in rivers that flow through large villages and towns, such as Menongue, doubtless causes many cases of diarrhoea. All towns in the Basin area of Angola lack safe supplies of treated water, and very few homes have toilets.

Key points

- About 600,000 people live in the catchment in Angola and close to the river and Delta in Kavango and Ngamiland. However, most other people in Angola, Namibia and Botswana live far away from the Basin.

- Populations in Kavango and Ngamiland grew by about 3% each year over the past 90 years. However, growth rates in Kavango over the last three decades were about 5% per year because of high rates of immigration from Angola.

- People in the Basin have been extremely mobile as a result of hostilities in Angola or from the desire to improve their livelihoods by moving to towns or other areas outside the Basin.

- There are few functional health and education services in Angola, whereas most people in Ngamiland and Kavango have access to health facilities and schools. Fertility and mortality rates in Angola are much higher than in the rest of the Basin.

- The most important health problems in the Basin are malaria, HIV/AIDS, acute respiratory infections, diarrhoea, scabies, tuberculosis, malnutrition and bilharzia.

135

8
FARMING

Food, income and security

What does the future hold for people with livelihoods deeply rooted in farming?

PEOPLE USE LAND and its resources in the Okavango Basin in a variety of ways, but much more land is used for farming than for any other purpose. Many more people also have livelihoods based on agriculture than on any other activity. Farming is not a simple enterprise, however. The host of factors that limit its success can be divided into two groups: those associated with the natural environment (soil quality, rainfall, evaporation and diseases and pests) and those constraints of a socio-economic nature (mainly household labour, availability of land, and access to other income). Alone, or in combination, these factors result in farmers being successful in some places, or in certain years, but not in others. Crops grow well in one area, but not elsewhere, for example. Rain often falls too irregularly to support good growth, and high rates of evaporation mean that water is often lost rapidly. Grasses vary in abundance and nutritional quality, and fires destroy hundreds of square kilometres of pastures on which livestock depend. Livestock diseases limit the vigour of the animals and restrict marketing opportunities. Some people rely heavily on farming for most or all their food needs whereas others are fortunate to have alternative sources of sustenance and income. Similarly, a few people can sell farm products if their farms are close to urban areas and customers with surplus cash. Many other farmers have little chance of marketing surpluses.

Residents of the Okavango Basin have faced these and other factors over many generations, and farmers have tuned their practices in ways to reduce the effects of the constraints. They have also found ways of exploiting occasional new opportunities. And since the constraints and opportunities vary across the Basin, we see different strategies and practices in different areas. In broad terms, the value of farming varies from the north to the south, much like the gradient of high to low rainfall (see page 63). Angolans are much more reliant on farming as a major source of food than people in Kavango and Ngamiland. In those two countries, a large number of people farm but the value of incomes from wages, remittances, pensions and other cash sources greatly exceeds that of farming. These are some of the issues explored in *Farming: food, income and security*.

The farmers

Small-scale farmers dominate farming activity in the Basin: there may be about 60,000 such farmers in Angola, 18,000 along the river in Kavango and 8,500 farming households close to the Delta in Ngamiland.[1]

Each household normally cultivates a few hectares and sometimes keeps small herds of cattle and goats. Probably 95% or more of all farming is practiced on roughly this basis. Most of the farmers live in rural areas concentrated in villages in Angola and Ngamiland or strung out along the river in Kavango. South and away from the Okavango and Delta in Kavango and Ngamiland are several hundred commercial farmers who have large herds of cattle. Some of them also have big fields of millet, but their farming activities have little or no association with the river. There are also several larger irrigation projects at Musese, Vungu Vungu, Shadikongoro, Shitemo, Bagani and Samochima, which mainly produce maize, cotton and wheat. Between them, these farms irrigate only about 1,200 hectares, but much bigger irrigation projects are planned in Kavango (see page 163).[2]

True subsistence farming is only practiced by the poorest households, who live mainly on the food they harvest with some additional fare coming from fish, honey and wild fruits. At the other end of the socio-economic scale are the many wealthier homes that live largely on bought food. Much of their income comes from wages or business profits. They, too, live in rural areas where the homes and farms look much the same as those of neighbouring subsistence farmers. Farm harvests provide supplementary food for the families of these richer farmers, but they also invest surplus cash in their farms to enhance their security. Most of their investments are in the form of livestock.

The focus on these two categories of farmers helps to introduce the wide spectrum of farming interests in the Basin. There is, of course, a complete gradient of wealth groups in between. The great majority of poor, subsistence farmers are in Angola, while proportions of farmers across the different wealth categories are more evenly spread in Kavango and Ngamiland. For example, only about 10% of farmers live mainly from their own farming produce in Ngamiland.[3]

Several household conditions and farming activities vary in clear relation to household wealth. Richer farmers tend to have larger households, their homes have a number of sources of cash income (e.g. wages, pensions, remittances, business activities), and they have several big fields and large numbers of livestock **(Figure 42)**. Men usually head such households. At the other end of the scale, women are often the heads of subsistence households where families, cultivated areas, and livestock holdings are small.

Wealthier farmers also tend to be more successful in producing better yields. They may buy improved seed

Most fields along the Cubango/Okavango are farmed manually on soils partially formed by repeated flooding long ago.

cultivars and farm implements, hire tractors, and fence their fields to prevent losses from stray animals. Richer farmers are also better able to supply a key input for farming: labour. Such manpower – more usually womanpower – is provided by their larger families and by hiring local hands when needed. 'When needed' is important because there are several critical periods when lots of work is required: to clear and plough fields before the first good rains fall so that planting can begin immediately, to thin young seedlings, weed the fields, and to harvest crops before they spoil or are lost to pests. All these jobs have to be done quickly, and at just the right time. Total amounts of time spent on crop production are impressive: about

Several ingredients are required to produce crops: cleared land, soil nutrients, water and labour. The last of these is often the most critical, especially in having enough labour available at appropriate times to weed and harvest.

Figure 42
Larger households have bigger herds of cattle and goats than smaller homes in Kavango (top) and people with bigger fields also have larger herds of cattle in Ngamiland (bottom).[4]

Average number of livestock

Number of people per household

Percentage

Hectare

270 hours of work per hectare of *molapo* field and 175 hours per hectare of dry-land field in Ngamiland, and 100–160 hours per hectare of dry-land field in Kavango (*molapo* and dry-land fields are described on page 145). Weeding is especially critical, labour intensive and time consuming. Frequencies of weeding vary, depending on the severity of weed infestation, type of crop and availability of labour, but fields are usually weeded two or three times per season in Angola, and once or twice in Ngamiland and Kavango.

Farm produce

Crop farming is dominated by four staple foods: pearl millet (*mahangu* in Kavango, *masangu* in Angola and *lebelebele* in Ngamiland), maize, sorghum and manioc (also called cassava). Much more land and effort is devoted to these staples than to other vegetable and fruit crops (mainly beans,

melons, pumpkins, cabbages, and tomatoes), groundnuts, sugar cane and bananas. Vegetables and fruit are grown more commonly in Angola than in the drier downstream areas. New crops of maize, millet and sorghum are planted each year, but manioc grows – and can be harvested – over three or four years. Its production is thus more reliable than that of the three cereals, but manioc tubers have poor nutritional value because they provide little protein. Sorghum is used both as a staple cereal food and to produce beer.

The mix and dominance of staple crops varies across the Basin in a rather clear way, and again this follows the gradient of rainfall across the region **(Figure 43)**. Maize, supplemented by manioc, is the main crop in the north-western Cubango sub-Basin. A greater variety of crops is grown in this wetter area, where farmers also benefit from more fertile soils than in most other areas. Manioc predominates in the Cuito sub-

The four main cereal crops in the Basin: millet (top left), manioc (top right), sorghum (bottom left) and maize (bottom right).

Figure 43

Crop production falls into four broad zones: maize predominates in the north-west, manioc in the north-eastern catchment of the Cuito, millet in the middle zone centered on Kavango, while similar areas of millet, maize and sorghum are planted in the Delta.

Predominantly maize
Predominantly manioc
Predominantly millet
Mixed maize, sorghum and millet

Millet (above) is the only cereal that grows well on nutrient-poor sandy soils in areas where rainfall is low and unpredictable. Ears of millet are threshed (opposite top) before the grain is ground and ready for cooking. Sugar cane (opposite bottom) is grown commonly on onaka fields in higher rainfall areas in Angola.

Basin, but maize and vegetables (planted in floodplain fields) are important supplements in this zone. Both maize and sorghum require rather high levels of soil moisture and thus grow only in areas of higher rainfall, or on patches subject to partial flooding or in clayey soils that retain more water than sand. Moving south-east, maize gradually declines in importance and is increasingly replaced by millet. This is the characterizing feature of the third zone, extending from about Caiundu all the way to the Delta. Millet is the only cereal that can grow productively in poor quality sandy soils where rainfall is relatively low. About 95% of cultivated land in Kavango is planted with millet, while only small patches of more clayey soil are used for maize and sorghum. Farmers around the Delta plant roughly equal proportions of millet, maize and sorghum, but the maize and sorghum is mainly planted in low-lying, clayey soils moistened by rain or rising floodwaters. Many of these soils are very fertile (see page 44).

Getting the time right

Crop farming is largely a summer activity since this is when most rain falls **(Figure 44)**. There are two reasons why timing is important. First, the shorter the season the more important it is for planting to follow the first good rains immediately. This is particularly critical in the southern areas where the rain season is much shorter than in Angola. Thus, farmers in Kavango and Ngamiland need to prepare their fields early so that their crops can be planted in December before the best and most frequent rains that normally fall in January and February. Delays in planting result in a greater chance of crops being short of water later on once the rains tail off. In Angola, by contrast, good rains can fall at any time between November and April, and planting can follow any of several adequate falls during early summer. Angolan farmers can also plant more than once, a possibility seldom available to people in Kavango and Ngamiland. Overall, the shorter season in the south gives less flexibility, making it more important to get the timing of planting, weeding and harvesting right.

A second reason for crop production to be timed carefully is to avoid sporadic dry periods. Again, such shortages of rain are more frequent and last longer in the southern areas, where crops also suffer from higher evaporation rates than those in Angola. An example of a long dry and hot spell is given in **Figure 45**.

Careful timing of crop growth is more critical for dry-land fields than those in floodplains and sodden valleys, where the ground remains wet for much longer. *Molapo* fields in Ngamiland are planted as the floodwaters begin dropping, normally in September

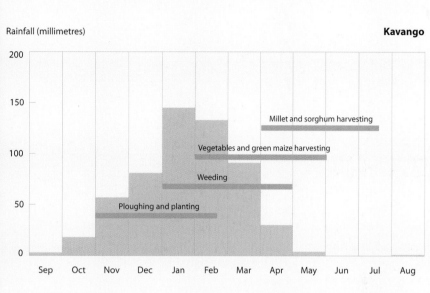

Rainfall (millimetres)   **Kavango**

- Millet and sorghum harvesting
- Vegetables and green maize harvesting
- Weeding
- Ploughing and planting

Sep Oct Nov Dec Jan Feb Mar Apr May Jun Jul Aug

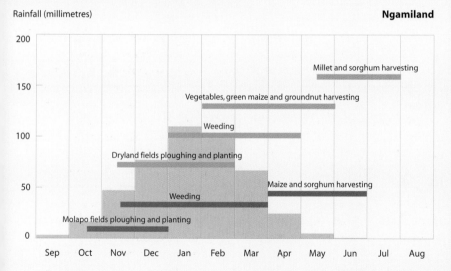

Rainfall (millimetres)   **Ngamiland**

- Millet and sorghum harvesting
- Vegetables, green maize and groundnut harvesting
- Weeding
- Dryland fields ploughing and planting
- Weeding
- Maize and sorghum harvesting
- Molapo fields ploughing and planting

Sep Oct Nov Dec Jan Feb Mar Apr May Jun Jul Aug

Figure 44

Summaries of crop farming activities in Kavango and around the Delta in
Ngamiland. The horizontal bars show when most activities take place, while
average monthly rainfall figures at Rundu and Maun provide perspectives on how
farming events relate to seasonal rainfall. Equivalent information is not available for
Angola where many more kinds of crops are grown, the timing of activities is more
flexible because of the long rain season and use of wet soils, and some crops are
harvested several times. Farming activities in the most northerly, high rainfall areas
also differ substantially from those further south in Angola.

Sorghum (left) *is brewed into beer or consumed as a cereal food. The nutrient value of manioc (below) is low, but it grows more reliably than millet, sorghum and maize and is thus a useful staple food. Ground manioc must be dried before it can be stored for later use (bottom).*

Rainfall (millimetres)   Temperature (degrees Celsius)

80   80

60   60

40   40

20   20

0   0

December 2000   January 2001   February 2001

Figure 45

Spells of hot, dry weather have devastating impacts on crops. The graph shows rainfall (blue bars) and maximum temperatures (brown bars) each day during December 2000 and January and February 2001 at Rundu. A total of 53 millimetres of rain fell over a few days in the third week of December 2000 when many fields of millet were planted. Much of the next six weeks were then dry, with a total of only 33 millimetres falling during a few scattered showers. It was also very hot, and maximum temperatures rose above 30°C on 39 of the 42 days. Relief eventually came in a spell of cool and wet weather in the last three weeks of February, but most crops planted earlier in December had died by then.

and October. Their clay soils hold moisture from the floods for several weeks and – with luck – are then dampened again by rain in November and December.

Crop seasons during the 1960s and in the 1980s and 1990s were often drier than in other decades (see page 64), and many farmers in Ngamiland switched from maize and sorghum to grow more millet during those dry years.[5] The Botswana government also responded by proclaiming droughts, enabling farmers to benefit from subsidies on the cost of seeds and ploughing. A total of 27 of the 33 years between 1964 and 1997 were declared to be drought years,[6] an amazing total for an area where dry periods are a regular and normal occurrence.

Farm lands

The vast majority of farming is on dry-land fields where crops are not irrigated and where their growth depends entirely on rain for moisture. Other crops grown using river water include those on the irrigation schemes described above, a few small vegetable gardens belonging to small-scale farmers who irrigate by hand, and numerous *onaka* (in Angola) and *molapo* fields (in Ngamiland). Both are placed close to rivers or streams where the soils are moistened by flooding or the drainage of water into low-lying ground. It is curious that *onaka*- or *molapo*-type fields are not used in Kavango. Maize in Angola is often grown on large *onaka* fields on floodplains, and floodwaters also inundate low-lying soils on *molapo* fields in Ngamiland. *Molapo* fields are either crescent-shaped around islands or elongate rectangles on the margins of river channels in the Delta. About 25% of crop areas around the

Delta are *molapo* fields and the rest are dry-land fields. Maize is the main crop on *molapo* fields, other crops being sorghum, groundnuts, beans, melons and pumpkins. Another kind of *onaka* field is common in small stream valleys in Angola, where the bottomlands of the valleys are sodden. The fields are really very small plots in which vegetables, sugar cane, and bananas are grown. Farmers often dig irrigation canals to divert stream water around the plots.

One of the greatest constraints to farming is the overall poor quality of soils. Although a variety of soils are found in the area, most are poorly suited to crops and much the largest area is covered by Kalahari sands that are low in nutrients, such as nitrogen, potassium and phosphorous. Rainwater also drains through the sands rapidly and so they retain little water. Better soils are generally found in lower lying depressions alongside the rivers and streams or in fossil drainage lines. These soils are more clayey and thus retain reasonable levels of moisture. The most nutrient-rich soils are in the Delta where they were formed by the progressive accumulation of minerals washed down into the floodplains of this wetland. Soils in the north-western Cubango sub-Basin are generally deep and well-drained. However, their nutrient content is relatively low and they can only be farmed for a few years before their fertility is exhausted.

The sizes of fields vary greatly, with wealthier and larger households generally having bigger fields. Field areas also depend much on the availability of good soils on unused land. In Angola, dry-land fields appear to be considerably bigger than the average dry-field areas of between two and five hectares in Kavango and Ngamiland. *Onaka* fields cultivated on floodplains in Angola often cover several hectares, but other *onaka* fields in small valleys and *molapo* fields in Ngamiland seldom exceed one hectare per family.

The extent to which fields are fenced varies to a great extent. Most fields are not enclosed and livestock owners thus have to provide herders to ensure that animals do not stray into fresh crops. However, wealthier farmers often fence their fields because they can buy fencing wire or have labour to erect fences of poles, branches or other natural materials. Fences are extremely uncommon in Angola and rather scarce in Kavango, in contrast to Ngamiland where the majority of fields have been fenced, often with the help of government and donor programs.

Farmland in Angola is apparently privately owned and can thus be bought and sold, but it is not clear to what degree legal titles are involved. All land used for agriculture elsewhere in the Basin in Kavango and Ngamiland belongs either to the state or is reserved for traditional, communal or tribal use by rural people.

There are three major kinds of fields in the Basin: onaka fields in Angola (top), molapo fields in Ngamiland (right) and widespread dry-land fields (below).

Traditional rights of succession are upheld in both countries. Local headmen play a much stronger role in allocating land for small-scale farming and grazing in Kavango than in Ngamiland where the Land Board regulates such rights for dry land fields (*molapo* fields are still allocated through traditional tenure systems). Thus, most small-scale farms are registered with land

boards in Ngamiland, while similar boards are now being established in Namibia. However, influential people in all three countries are obtaining large farms to an increasing extent. People who negotiate and acquire documents in Luanda to give them rights over farms have expropriated large tracts of farmland in Angola, while wealthier civil servants, businessmen and politicians have obtained large cattle farms to the south of the river and Delta in Kavango and Ngamiland.[7]

The extent of land cleared for crop farming is impressive, especially around the western and southern margins of the Delta and on the Kavango side of the Okavango where little land remains in its natural condition **(Figure 46)**. Much less ground has been cleared north of the Okavango on the Angolan side of the river and further north. However, massive expanses of land have been cleared around the bigger towns

Trees and brush are burnt to help clear new fields. However, the fires often run wild and then burn large areas of surrounding woodlands, pastures and floodplains.

Figure 46
Approximately 4.2% of the catchment and within 20 kilometres of the river and Delta in Kavango and Ngamiland has been cleared for crops (dark brown areas). Much of this land has been abandoned because the soils are no longer sufficiently fertile. About 26,000 hectares had been cleared in Kavango in 1943, 72,100 hectares in 1972 and 194,500 hectares in 1996, an average annual rate of increase between 1943 and 1996 of 3.9%.[8]

in Angola, such as Menongue, Kubango, Cuchi, Mumbué, Cuito Cuanavale and Chitembo. These and other expanses of cleared land show up clearly in the satellite image on page 16. Similarly, the many people living in the central highlands are responsible for the large clearings in the extreme north-west of the catchment. The large clearings in Angola are also due to the rapid rate at which land is cleared and then cultivated for four to six years before new fields are cleared. As more and more land becomes useless for crops, farmers have to search for virgin soils further away from their villages. Thus, farm workers in larger villages often have to walk 10 to 15 kilometres each day out to their fields and then back home again. Thirty and more years ago, fields were apparently re-used after rest periods of up to 20 years, but fallow periods now seldom last more than seven years because of the shortage of alternative cropland nearby.

This slash-and-burn, shifting cultivation is possible in Angola because soils suitable for crops are broadly distributed, and water is also fairly widely available. By contrast, most arable soils are close to the river in Kavango and the Delta in Ngamiland, and there is little water away from these areas. The majority of people are therefore concentrated close to their fields, although some Kavango farmers have cleared new fields far south of the river where borehole water has recently been supplied. The many other farmers who remain near the river and Delta simply have little chance of clearing new fields on unused soils, and they have to continue using fields that have lost much of their fertility. This is one reason why yields (see below) are so low, and one would expect that farmers would apply manure and/or fertilizers to their fields. However, efforts to boost soil fertility are very limited. Along the river in Kavango, only 2% and 8% of households apply fertilizers and compost, respectively, and only 16 – 22% of farmers apply manure to their fields.[9] Figures for Ngamiland are not available but all indications again suggest that fertilizers, compost and manure are hardly used.

Variable success and high risks

From the account given so far it should be clear that this is not great farming country, mainly because most soils are poor in quality and rainfall is often in short supply. Crop productivity is therefore very low compared to that in most other areas of central and southern Africa. Conditions are nevertheless better in the northern areas of the Basin than in the south, a trend reflected by yields that are usually higher in the north. The only information known to us indicates harvests of between 500 and 700 kilograms of maize per hectare in Angola, more than double average yields of 100–160 kilograms in Kavango and Ngamiland. Smaller differences hold for millet: 250 kilograms per hectare in Angola versus 100–150 kilograms in Kavango and Ngamiland.[10] The other area where yields are high are on the *molapo* fields around the Delta as a result of the much more fertile soils (see page 44). One study found that *molapo* fields produced 2,100 kilograms per hectare versus 250 kilograms on nearby dry-land fields (the figure of 250 kilograms is higher than the averages given above, perhaps because the survey was done in a good season).[11]

A government irrigation scheme overlooking Popa Falls.

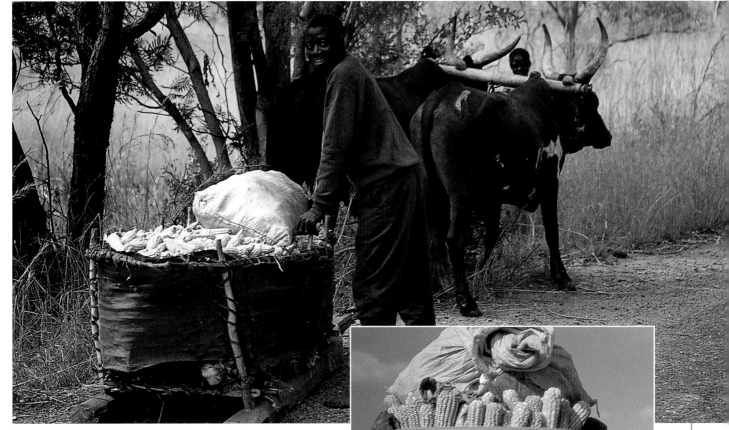

Good harvests of maize require large containers, in this case a basket made of red bark on a sledge in Angola (top). *The results of more modest yields can be carried home in a bucket* (right).

These average figures mask the high levels of variation from year to year that are characteristic of the area. Some seasons see good yields as a result of abundant, well-spaced rainfall and few pests, while in other seasons the yields are so low that farmers do not bother to harvest. Over and above problems of poor soils and rainfall, crops also face damage from diseases, insects (such as locusts), and birds (redbilled quelea finches). Elephants and other wildlife may be a problem in certain areas.

Except for *molapo* fields, crop farming in the southern Basin is apparently an unproductive business. But it is also true that yields would be higher if farmers made more effort, for example by fertilizing the soil, weeding more often, and fencing off their crops. Why should crop farming be so unproductive? One answer may lie in the idea that crop farming evolved over hundreds of years as something of a secondary, somewhat complementary activity. This was because farming was practised in an area where there was a relative abundance of other foods in the form of fish, wild fruits and animals to be hunted. With such alternatives there would be little need to invest heavily in crops, especially if the risks of failure were high, rewards from selling or bartering surpluses were low, and a high burden of disease meant that people could not work harder. Under these conditions it was perhaps prudent to invest less effort in crops and more effort in obtaining other foods. The availability of most of these

Harvests are often stored in large constructions made from poles, grass, reeds or papyrus and sealed with mud and dung. These storage huts are in Kavango (left) and Angola (right).

other foods has decreased, of course, but the decline has been compensated by new cash incomes with which to buy food, at least in Kavango and Ngamiland. The value of crops was thus first overshadowed by food from the bush, and now it is surpassed by food from shops and markets.[12]

Livestock: income or security

Much of this chapter has concentrated on crop farming, an activity practiced by most rural households. Field sizes, crops and harvests vary from farmer to farmer but the variation is nothing like the huge differences between households when it comes to livestock farming. Figures for Angola are not available, but it is clear that a tiny proportion of farmers have cattle, perhaps less than 5%. (Almost no information is available for livestock farming in Angola and most of the material below refers to Kavango and Ngamiland.) Roughly half of all households have cattle or goats in Kavango and Ngamiland. Of course, half of all rural people therefore have no access to benefits from these animals **(Figure 47)**. The same is true for other animals, such as donkeys, sheep and pigs: some people own these animals, many others not at all, and amongst those that are livestock farmers there is great variation in herd or flock size. In general, wealthier farmers with large households have the biggest numbers of cattle and goats, while poorer households have no livestock.

Cattle and goats are much more abundant compared to pigs, sheep and donkeys. It is hard to estimate the total number of animals in and immediately around the

river system because no information is available for Angola. However, there may be about 150,000 cattle and 140,000 goats in the Basin.[13] Most Angolan cattle are in the southern half of the catchment apparently because various diseases, especially those carried by ticks, limit cattle farming in the northern catchment. There are thus few cattle even though there are many more farmers than in the south. Many Angolan families also lost their cattle to pillaging soldiers during the last few decades of strife. Perhaps animal numbers will increase as life returns to normal.

Before the drilling of boreholes most animals were concentrated close to the river system in Kavango and Ngamiland. Nowadays there are large herds to the south of the river in Kavango and south and west of the Delta in Ngamiland. These animals are either kept at cattle-posts in open communal or tribal areas, or on large fenced farms allocated to individual farmers (see below). Cattle numbers in both countries have increased greatly over the past 100 years, largely as a result of better control of diseases and an increasing number of relatively wealthy people acquiring herds. However, there have also been several sporadic and temporary declines, particularly after the very dry years in 1986–1987, 1992–1993 and 1995–1996 in both countries **(Figure 48)**. The most notable decrease occurred after the 1995 outbreak of lung sickness (or CBPP, Contagious Bovine Pleuropneumonia) in Ngamiland where a total of 320,000 cattle were slaughtered early in 1996 to control the outbreak. Numbers have since increased as people have slowly built up their herds.

Percentage **Cattle**

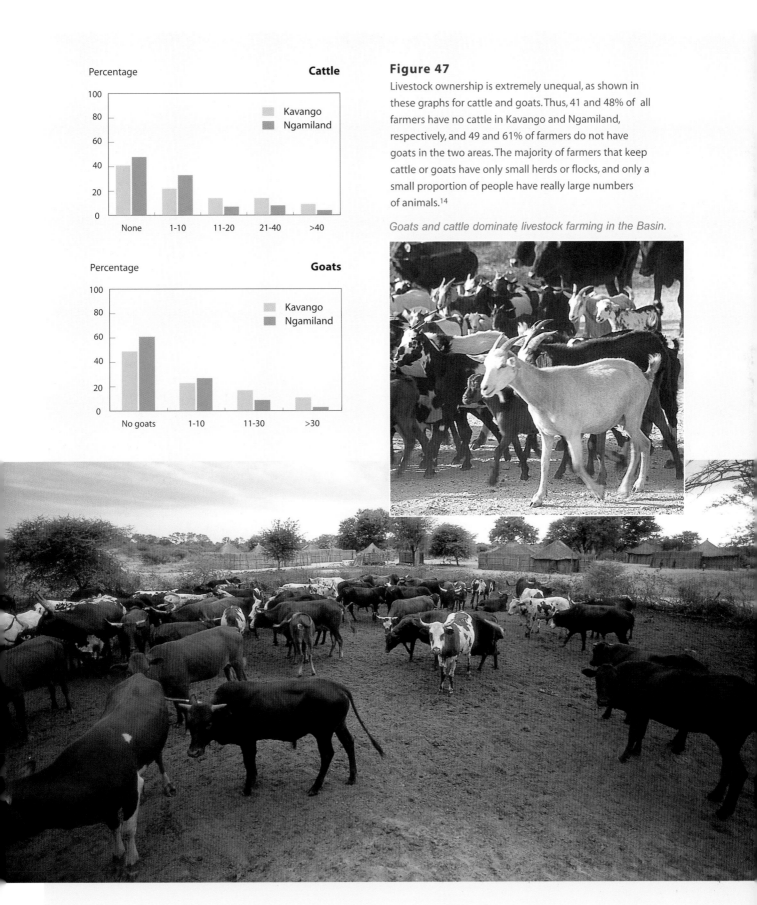

Figure 47

Livestock ownership is extremely unequal, as shown in these graphs for cattle and goats. Thus, 41 and 48% of all farmers have no cattle in Kavango and Ngamiland, respectively, and 49 and 61% of farmers do not have goats in the two areas. The majority of farmers that keep cattle or goats have only small herds or flocks, and only a small proportion of people have really large numbers of animals.[14]

Goats and cattle dominate livestock farming in the Basin.

Percentage **Goats**

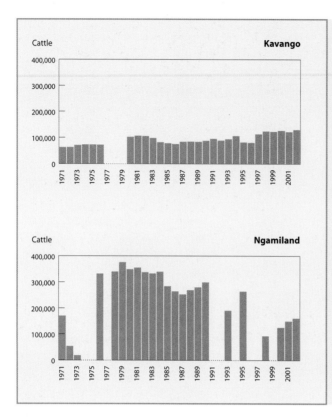

Figure 48

Cattle numbers have been increasing in Ngamiland and Kavango over the past several decades, although there have been several declines as a result of prolonged periods of low rainfall, for example in 1987 in Ngamiland and 1995 in Kavango. All cattle were eradicated in 1996 in Ngamiland to control an outbreak of lung sickness. The figures are for the whole Kavango region and Ngamiland district, since separate figures for numbers close to the river system are not available. We think, however, that most increases occurred away from the river and that livestock numbers have been rather constant close to the Okavango and Delta. Dotted lines show years for which data are missing.[15]

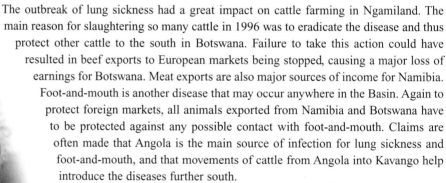

The outbreak of lung sickness had a great impact on cattle farming in Ngamiland. The main reason for slaughtering so many cattle in 1996 was to eradicate the disease and thus protect other cattle to the south in Botswana. Failure to take this action could have resulted in beef exports to European markets being stopped, causing a major loss of earnings for Botswana. Meat exports are also major sources of income for Namibia. Foot-and-mouth is another disease that may occur anywhere in the Basin. Again to protect foreign markets, all animals exported from Namibia and Botswana have to be protected against any possible contact with foot-and-mouth. Claims are often made that Angola is the main source of infection for lung sickness and foot-and-mouth, and that movements of cattle from Angola into Kavango help introduce the diseases further south.

Whatever the cause of infection, disease control in Namibia and Botswana is serious business. Both countries use several measures to control lung sickness, foot-and-mouth and other diseases. The first consists of vaccination campaigns conducted in both Kavango and Ngamiland against foot-and-mouth, lung sickness, blackquarter, anthrax and brucellosis. A second measure is the series of fences to prevent or control the movement of cattle (and all other large mammals, both domestic and wild) from moving south of the 'vaccination zone' **(Figure 50)**. The fences have stopped the movements of large game in Botswana, causing the death of many animals and, as a consequence, frequent protests by environmentalists. Other fences have been erected within Ngamiland to contain the movement of cattle in case of an outbreak of disease, and also to stop contact between cattle and buffalo in the Delta. This is the main purpose of the so-called northern and southern buffalo fence. Herds of buffalo that occasionally stray out of the Delta are driven back using helicopters.

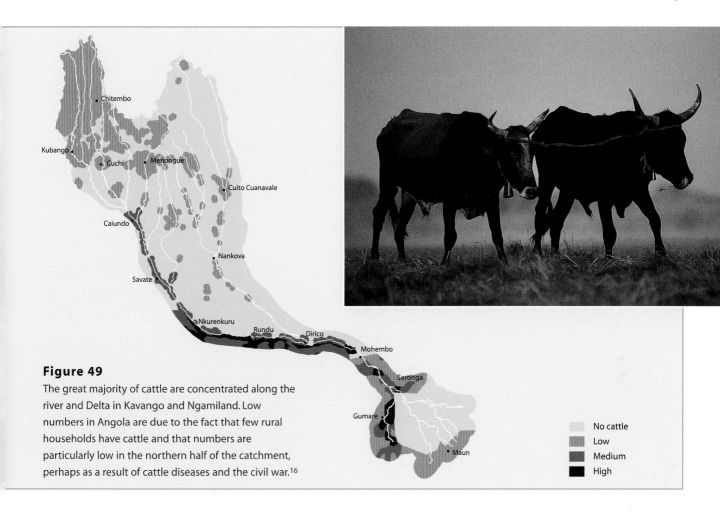

Figure 49

The great majority of cattle are concentrated along the river and Delta in Kavango and Ngamiland. Low numbers in Angola are due to the fact that few rural households have cattle and that numbers are particularly low in the northern half of the catchment, perhaps as a result of cattle diseases and the civil war.[16]

No cattle
Low
Medium
High

The last major collapse of cattle numbers before the 1996 eradication programme was in 1897 when the great rinderpest epidemic apparently killed most cattle. Large numbers of wildlife were also killed by rinderpest. An interesting consequence of this was that tsetse fly largely disappeared from Ngamiland over two decades. The flies suck blood from cattle, other animals and humans and, by doing so transmit sleeping sickness to people and trypanosomiasis to cattle (see page 123). Although few cattle contract this disease these days, it remains a serious potential threat to cattle farming.

Livestock bring a range of benefits to people fortunate enough to own them: draught power provided by oxen and donkeys, milk, leather and meat. However, for many farmers their main benefit is in providing security and investment values, much like other people put their savings into property, shares or investment accounts. This is not surprising in semi-arid areas where crop farming is so unreliable, and where livestock are much less vulnerable to shortages of rain. Little labour is required to look after animals, and returns from time spent on labour for livestock are greater than returns from crops. Animals are also a ready source of cash when money is needed to buy household goods and food when crops fail, and to cater for special family needs.

Investing in cattle is particularly important for farmers who are relatively wealthy as a result of good wages or earnings from businesses. Many of these farmers (usually 'weekend farmers') in Kavango and Ngamiland have acquired large herds and ranches away from the river and Delta. Examples of these are the TGLP (Tribal Grazing Land Policy) ranches in Botswana, and the Mangetti and other farms allocated by tribal Land and Farming Committees in Kavango. Some of these farms were given out to reduce pressure on communal pastures and with the hope that the farmers would manage their herds on a commercial basis. However, rates of selling are way below these expectations, and off-take rates in both countries remain low, as indicated by these figures:

Annual off-take of cattle, goats and sheep sold in Kavango and Ngamiland.[17]

	Kavango	Ngamiland
Cattle	7%	7.4 – 12.8%
Goats	8%	6.5 – 12%
Sheep	No information	5.7 – 13.1

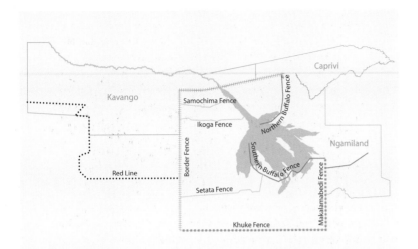

Figure 50

A series of fences divide up Ngamiland and Kavango to control the movement of cattle and other animals. The 'red-line' fence in Namibia and the Khuke and Makalamabedi fences in Ngamiland are veterinary fences to separate the northern vaccination zones from southern ranching areas, while the two buffalo fences prevent contact between cattle and buffalo in the Delta. Border fences prevent cattle movements between Namibia and Botswana. The Samochima, Ikoga and Setata fences are intended to contain cattle movements in the event of an outbreak of lung sickness or foot-and-mouth. All these fences additionally help control the spread of other contagious diseases such as bovine tuberculosis and brucellosis. The fences restrict the movements of wildlife, and this has led to fierce protests and debate on whether the benefits of controlling livestock diseases outweigh the damage done to wildlife.

Two thirds of Kavango cattle sales go to informal markets while the other third is sold to MEATCO (a commercial meat processing enterprise). The highest off-takes in Ngamiland occurred in the driest years, presumably because animals were sold that might otherwise have died or suffered from shortages of grazing. Farmers often argue that they would sell more cattle if controls restricting sales south of the veterinary cordon fences were lifted. It is usually the owners of large herds that argue this apparently logical point. However, sales in Kavango did not increase when prices offered north of the Red Line were increased to comparable amounts paid elsewhere in Namibia. Most animals sold in Kavango also belong to people with small herds, while those with large herds make few of their cattle or goats available for sale. Despite all of this, one might expect that the growing cash economy would oblige farmers to sell more animals to provide them with additional cash.

Changing lifestyles

Rural livelihoods have changed greatly over the past 100 years, and the changes continue in more rapid, complex and varied ways than we often recognize. Most changes were introduced by colonial influences that brought new values and aspirations associated with religion and education, longer lives as a result of health care, and cash incomes from migrant labour and government jobs. Just 75 years ago, few people had any schooling and most had never benefitted from modern medicine. Not many people had seen or heard of sources of energy such as electricity, gas or paraffin, and there were very few cars or roads, and no public telephones. There was little experience in having cash incomes or in buying food, and most people were wholly and directly dependant on resources offered by the natural environment.

In Botswana and Namibia, developments that improved the lives of people continued after independence. Some of the most significant changes were those making urban jobs and businesses much more lucrative than rural farms. Enormous attractions and pressures encourage people to abandon lives as rural farmers, and many people have responded by moving to Maun, Rundu and urban centres outside the Basin. By contrast, rural people in south-eastern Angola have been through three recent decades of hostile upheaval: whole villages abandoned and destroyed (see page 58), and many men and young boys wrenched away by the armed forces. Many fields could not be tended properly for fear of anti-personnel landmines. Most of the few schools and clinics in Angola closed down. New changes now confront many Angolans: to find jobs as economic activity picks up or to become rural farmers, often in new villages around which they must clear new fields.

Livelihoods have also changed because of a loss of natural resources, mainly as a result of reduced material incomes from hunting, fishing and the gathering of resources from wild plants, such as fruit. A hundred years ago there was abundant wildlife, probably comparable to the numbers of hippos, lechwe, giraffe and other mammals now seen only in the Mahango and Moremi Game Reserves and in parts of the Delta (see page 114). Reminders of successful hunts in the past are embodied in traditional poems and songs that pay tribute to hunting forays in Kavango. Fish populations along the river between Angola and Kavango have declined (see page 100). Crop yields may also have dropped, especially along the river and around larger towns and villages in Angola. The repeated use of fields, with little use of fertilizers, manure or compost to replenish soil nutrients, has meant that soil fertility has declined. The growing number of people has also limited the area in which new fields can be cleared. Overstocking has led to the loss of pastures. In Kavango, there has also been a decline in incomes from livestock because there are now far fewer cattle in relation to the number of people than before.[18]

Household welfare, and new incomes

Most rural homes look rather similar, and this is one reason why it is often assumed that the majority of rural people live and subsist in similar ways. However, rural households vary greatly in overall wealth. Each household also depends on a different mix of incomes from agricultural holdings (livestock and fields), natural resources (grazing, water, fertile soils, and fish) and cash sources (wages, business earnings, remittances and pensions). A few figures on ownership and access to assets confirm the high degree of variation between households. For example, cattle are owned by a tiny proportion of homes in Angola, 59% of households in

Kavango and 52% in Ngamiland. In Kavango, approximately 6% of all farmers own about half the cattle in the region, and about 270 people effectively own almost one quarter of all land in Kavango.[20] About 31% of homes in Ngamiland have no livestock of any kind.[21]

Many households have several different incomes, and even individuals often have several incomes as well. The following table shows that farming activities generate less than one fifth of all rural income in Kavango. Different kinds of employment, by contrast, provide almost two-thirds of an average household's income. The same study found that the annual income of a home in which one or more people were formally employed was seven times greater than that of a household in which no one was working elsewhere.

Fishing has been serious business for a long time. Charles John Andersson, the Swedish explorer and so-called discoverer of the Okavango River, wrote in 1861 'many of the natives devote a considerable portion of their time to fishing, and employ various simple, ingenious and highly effective contrivances for capturing the finny tribe'.[19]

Percentages of total household income from different sources in Kavango.[22]

Source	Percentage of total income
Crop production	10
Livestock	8
Non-agricultural resources	19
Non-government employment	50
Government employment	14
Total	100

Note: Non-agricultural resources include goods such as fish, wood, etc.

A different way of looking at household incomes is to ask what activities provide the main source of income. The following table provides such information for Ngamiland. Farming is the most important source of income for half the homes, while cash incomes from wages, salaries and small business activities are most important for 31% of households. The survey was conducted in 1997 when many households were receiving government assistance following the lung sickness eradication of cattle in 1996.

Percentages of total households having different main sources of income in Ngamiland.[23]

Source	Percentage of total income
Farming	50
Wages and salaries	25
Government assistance	16
Small business	5
Remittances	4
Total	100

Rural people could be expected to grow the great majority of their food. This is true in Angola where few rural people have jobs or businesses, but a survey found that farm produce (cereals, milk and meat) made up only half of the value of food consumed by rural homes in Kavango.[24] The other half was bought with cash. Cash resources have another great value: they open up a range of possibilities from which people without cash are totally excluded. Having cash allows you to pay for transport, school fees and uniforms, medical care and food, not only luxuries but also staples when your crop fails. Not surprisingly, there are great pressures on people to get a job or earn a business income. Much of the pressure is on young people who are urged to leave home in search of a job in Huambo, Menongue, Maun, Rundu, Luanda, Gaborone or Windhoek, for example. These are the places many people now go to, and where their children will want to be in the future.

In essence, most people are not keen to be rural farmers. And yet most plans for development in the Basin concentrate on rural development. Some plans seek to provide social services and infrastructure while others attempt to improve household economies. The latter largely concentrate on raising production on small farms to enhance food security and increase sales of farm products. All these efforts are founded on the assumption that rural livelihoods can really be improved. We think this assumption is dangerous, for the following reasons:

■ Promoting rural, subsistence livelihoods simply runs against the aspirations of most people.
■ Rural life in most areas is hard and insecure because of poor soils, low and unreliable rainfall, and the prevalence of disease. Services are also hard to come by.
■ Making a good living in this environment requires much more than the few hectares most people are expected to have.
■ There are few markets where farmers can sell their products to make some kind of reasonable income.
■ Finally, capital is required for effective, lucrative farming activities to develop. Small-scale farmers seldom have access to savings and their insecure tenure and meagre assets make it difficult to get loans.

These are all reasons that make rural development difficult, especially for subsistence farmers who face high risks and low rewards, and have better options elsewhere. For the time being, however, many rural people have little immediate hope of moving up the economic ladder, remaining stuck on the bottom rung where they eke out a living from farming, fishing and gathering. Compare these rural poor with people who have entered the modern economy, mostly as wage earners working as civil servants or businessmen. These are the Basin's 'movers and shakers' people setting the pace by taking command of much of the economy and the land. It is this 'elite' group who will determine much of the Basin's future.

People remaining as poor rural farmers should obviously not be abandoned. But efforts to support them will be more effective if they are appropriately cast in terms of poverty alleviation rather than as rural development. Effective development can then concentrate on urban areas and those options that recognize and capitalize on real benefits to be gained from rural environments, for example large-scale farming, tourism and the economic use of wildlife.

Farming and household livelihoods in three countries

Factors that affect farming practices and household livelihoods differ in many ways in the three countries. The following offers a comparative summary of the main features in the Angolan provinces, Kavango and Ngamiland.

Angola

Perhaps the best argument for trying to raise the development of rural people can be made in Angola where the great majority of people live in rural areas and depend heavily on agriculture for food. Luckily, Angola also offers the best conditions for crop farming. Most farmers grow maize as the principal staple food, with manioc and millet as supplements or, in certain areas, as the dominant crop. A great variety of vegetables, sugar cane and bananas are also grown. Many maize fields and vegetable gardens are, respectively, cultivated in floodplains and small valleys with rich, damp soils. Compared to most other areas in the Basin, the variety of crops is much greater, yields are higher, the soils are more fertile and hold more water, and higher rainfall over longer periods makes crop farming more flexible and less risky. Most people live in villages and tend surrounding dry-land fields, very few of which are fenced. Once fields have been used for several years, farmers clear new fields further from their villages because there is a relative abundance of water and soils suited to arable agriculture. Very large areas of cleared land therefore now lie abandoned. The few farmers with cattle live mainly in the southern parts of the catchment. The combined effects of decades of strife, insecurity, displacement and landmines (many surrounding villages) combine to present rural Angolans with enormous challenges.

Kavango

Much more information on farming and livelihoods is available for Kavango and Ngamiland than for the Angolan catchment. Although almost all rural people in Kavango engage in farming activities in Kavango, the value of incomes from crops and livestock are much lower than those they derive from wages, business earnings, pensions and remittances. Many households thus have family members earning incomes away from their farms. Millet is the predominant crop grown on fields of several hectares per family. The millet is mainly grown on sandy soils that are poor in nutrients. Some people tend small patches of maize and sorghum on low-lying clayey soils, but farmers do not use seasonally flooded areas for crops. Most fields are close to their owner's household, and a shortage of unused land with suitable soils means there is little chance of clearing new and better fields once soil nutrients are depleted. Yields of millet, maize and sorghum are very low, averaging 100 – 160 kilograms per hectare. Insufficient and badly timed rainfall, poor soils and a lack of effort to improve crop growth are the main reasons for such low yields. Approximately half of all households have cattle and goats, but less than 10% of these animals are sold each year, mainly because livestock are largely valued for the security and investments they bring to farmers.

Ngamiland

Farming conditions here are rather similar to those in Kavango: millet is the main crop on dry-land fields, many households have sources of cash income that exceed the value of farm earnings, roughly half of all homes have cattle and goats, sales of livestock are low, most soils are sandy and poor in quality, and farmers have little chance of finding better, unused areas on which to clear new fields. Millet crops also often fail as a result of shortages of rain. However, many farmers have *molapo* fields in seasonally flooded lowlands where the soil is fertile. Maize is the main crop and yields are much higher than on dry-land millet fields. Overall, farming appears to be taken more seriously than in Kavango: weeding is more frequent, most fields are fenced, and government subsidies and controls are more substantive. All cattle in Ngamiland were slaughtered in 1996 as part of a programme to control an outbreak of lung sickness. This and foot-and-mouth disease are controlled by veterinary fences and annual vaccinations in both Ngamiland and Kavango.

Key points

- The great majority of the 60 to 70 thousand rural households practise small-scale farming in the Angolan catchment and around the river in Kavango and Delta in Ngamiland.
- Most poorer subsistence farmers are in Angola, whereas many rural farming households in Kavango and Ngamiland also have cash incomes from other sources that far exceed the incomes they obtain from farming.
- Rainfall is higher and soils are generally better in Angola than elsewhere, and more maize, manioc, and vegetables are grown there than to the south where crops are dominated by millet.
- Livestock farming becomes progressively more important from north to south, and from the wettest upper catchment to the most arid areas around the Delta.
- Yields are higher in Angola than to the south where low and badly timed rainfall often makes crop farming unproductive and risky.
- Crops are only grown on rich soils in seasonally flooded areas close to the river, its tributaries and channels in Angola and Ngamiland.
- Farmers in Kavango and Ngamiland have little access to areas with good soils on which new crops can be grown, whereas Angolan farmers often move on to clear new fields once their fields have been used for several years.
- Lung sickness and foot-and-mouth disease may occur anywhere in the Basin. Veterinary fences and vaccinations in Kavango and Ngamiland control these and other diseases from spreading into areas from where meat is exported.

9

OKAVANGO

Challenges and opportunities

Up to 30,000 elephants frequent the waters of the Okavango.

BEFORE LOOKING FORWARDS it is useful to start with a glance backwards (much like the importance of understanding river flows upstream before considering how the Delta functions). First, some fundamental points that cover the whole Basin. The fact that much of the Okavango flows across flat Kalahari sands has several important consequences. Water flows are relatively slow and steady. Potentials for crop production are limited by the low nutrient content of the sands, and the supply of nutrients into the river water is very low. As a result, most of the Okavango's rivers have low fish stocks and numbers of wildlife. It is only in the Delta that biological production is rich because of the considerable accumulation of nutrients at the end of the river system.

People in the Basin have moved a great deal, and many continue doing so: trying to find jobs, business opportunities, better fields, greener pastures or access to water, or to escape hostilities. These are factors that determine where people are now, and where they will go in the future. Compared to surrounding areas in southern Africa, the number of people in the Basin is small. Although new forms of transport allow us to move in and out of the Basin within hours, the Okavango remains relatively remote from centres of economic and administrative activity in southern Africa. No minerals of economic importance are known in the Basin.

Second, what broad features characterize each country? Angola has the highest and most reliable falls of rain, the lowest evaporation rates, and many more rivers and streams than any other part of the Basin. Water is thus seldom a limiting factor, and it has much less value than further south where water becomes a precious, envied resource. Features of the soils, rocks and landscape in the western Cubango sub-Basin result in more rapid water flows than in the eastern Cuito catchment. Sediment and nutrient loads carried by the rivers are probably greater in the west, where there is also a greater potential for water-borne pollution as a result of the higher population.

Much of the Angolan Basin is pristine, occupied by small numbers of people who live close to the land. Parts of it have been rendered inhospitable by countless land mines, and the massive investment in warfare has been at the expense of development. Social conditions are very much poorer than further south, and services and infrastructure are in disarray. The most important use of the rivers is as a source of drinking and washing water, and for the moisture they bring to *onaka* fields (see page 146). Angola

appears to be trying to rebuild the country, but the Basin is unlikely to benefit from significant development for many years for the following reasons. The number of people in the Basin is a tiny fraction of the total Angolan population, and much of the Basin is remote and far from the 'vision' of decision-makers in Luanda. Priority will also be given to other parts of Angola that offer much greater potential for food production and economic gains. Also, while hostilities have ended, significant funds to develop the catchment will not be available as long as large-scale corruption and theft of Angola's riches continues.

The Namibian part of the Basin has been characterized by massive immigration from Angola, causing very rapid population growth, clearing of land and the loss of natural resources. As a result, a concentrated population now lives along the southern banks of the Cubango/Okavango River, and many others have moved far to the south of the river.[1] The river is really a waterway or channel, passing along and through the region. It is not surprising that most people see the water simply as a resource that comes in, goes out, and is there for the taking. This is true for the local inhabitants, who mainly use the river as a source of reeds for building material, water for domestic use and livestock, and as a fishing resource. It is also true for the Namibian government, which views the water as a source of energy for hydroelectric power, for agriculture, and to meet demands for water in urban areas elsewhere in the country. It also sees the valley of the Cubango/ Okavango River as having good potential for crop production. Several new large and expanded irrigation schemes are being developed, mainly to improve Namibia's food security and reduce dependency on food imports (see below).

Botswana is the final recipient of water produced in Angola and passed on by Namibia. The Delta is a colossal sink for the water, sediments and nutrients originating in Angola. The abundance of water and nutrients, and patterns of sediment deposition, give the Delta its diversity of habitats, wildlife riches and beauty. From these natural resources, considerable benefits are derived through the wildlife tourism industry: jobs, income, tax revenues, services and infrastructure, and international acclaim. This use of natural resources in Botswana is quite different from uses of the river elsewhere with the small exception of the few lodges and camps east of Rundu and around the Mahango Game Reserve in Kavango.

Botswana has invested heavily to make good use of the Delta's riches, and has gone to considerable lengths to ensure that the Delta and its wildlife resources remain healthy.

Pressures on the system

Although much of the Basin's environment is as natural as it ever was, the Okavango faces pressure from several processes: water abstraction, changes to water and sediment flow, pollution and changes to nutrient levels, loss of vegetation, soil erosion and fires. The biggest pressures are from the major towns and other areas of dense settlement **(Figure 51)**. This is where relatively large volumes of water are used, effluent may find its way into the river, and plant life is destroyed as a result of fields being cleared, the collection of building materials and fuel wood, and overgrazing.

Little water is now extracted from the river system, which is surprising since much of the Basin is so dry. No irrigation schemes pump water out of any of the rivers in Angola to our knowledge, and perhaps the only dam is a tiny one (about 40 hectares) on a tributary of the Cuebe at Menongue. None of the towns in Angola have bulk water supplies from the river, and it will probably be some years before pumped, treated water is provided to the towns. For example, the water supply system to Menongue was completed in 1974, but stopped working in 1977. Recent attempts to re-establish the scheme failed because most residents were unwilling to pay for water.

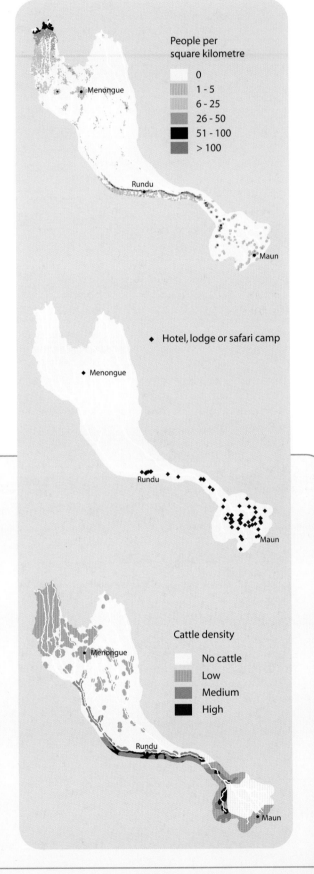

People per square kilometre

- 0
- 1 - 5
- 6 - 25
- 26 - 50
- 51 - 100
- > 100

◆ Hotel, lodge or safari camp

Cattle density

- No cattle
- Low
- Medium
- High

Figure 51

Uses of the Okavango vary greatly across the Basin, as reflected by differences in the number of people and cattle, location of accommodation for tourists, and placement of water supply and irrigation schemes. Sites where hydroelectric stations have been proposed are shown on the larger map.

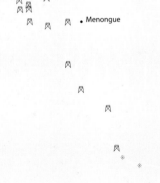

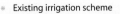

* Existing irrigation scheme

* Proposed irrigation scheme

⚒ Proposed hydro-electric scheme

⬦ Town water supply

About 22 million cubic metres (Mm³) (equivalent to 0,022 cubic kilometres) are now extracted from the river each year in Kavango. Approximately 74% of this supplies agricultural irrigation schemes, 15% is taken by rural people for their livestock, and 11% is used for Rundu.[2] The 22 Mm³ amounts to less than 0.25 of a percent of the total average volume of water that enters Botswana at Mohembo. Even during years and months with low flows, the volumes pumped are relatively small. About 1,100 hectares (ha) are now farmed under irrigation, the largest areas being at Shitemo (350 ha), Shadikongoro (266 ha), Musese (180 ha) and Bagani Prison farm (90 ha). However, new schemes or expansions are being developed to irrigate another 7,400 ha. Most of this is north of Mukwe (4,000 ha), while the rest is at Kangongo (2,000 ha), Ndonga (700 ha), Vungu Vungu (250 ha), Shadikongoro (180 ha), Musese (120 ha) and Shitemo (120 ha). Once implemented, these would raise the total amount of water extracted from the river to about 134 Mm³ per year, or 1.4% of all water that leaves Namibia. The proportion remains small but much irrigation water would be pumped at the start of the growing season in early summer when the river is at its lowest, and substantial proportions of water could be extracted during years when flows are unusually low.

Botswana extracts little surface water. There is one small irrigation scheme at Samochina, and water is piped to villages in and around Mohembo, Shakawe and from Sepopa down to Gumare. In total, these add up to about 2 Mm³. Small additional amounts are taken directly by livestock and for domestic purposes. Water supplies to Maun, Sehithwa, Tsau and Shorobe are all from underground sources replenished by seepage from the Delta. Taking all these uses and amounts together, Botswana probably uses less than 0.1% of all water entering the Delta each year.[3]

Perhaps more concern has been voiced about possible changes to patterns and levels of water flow than any other threat. These fears were foremost during the mid-1990s when Namibia considered pumping Okavango water to supply Windhoek. Similar fears are reflected in the common claim that the lack of high floodwaters during the past two decades (see page 86) was due to the alleged construction of dams in

Over 700 hectares of bush were cleared in 2003 for this new irrigation scheme at Ndonga. The farm is one of several new schemes being developed to improve Namibia's food security. Assessments of the environmental impacts of this farm and the programme to greatly expand food production using Okavango water for irrigation have not been done. The clearing is bordered by the Rundu-Divundu road on the right, the Omatako Omuramba below, and the Okavango River to the left.

Tens of thousands of people living along the rivers in Angola do their washing in them every day. The impacts of so much soap on water quality may not be serious because most soap molecules are broken down quite rapidly. More severe problems could arise as a result of infectious bacteria and other parasites finding their way into water, particularly when summer rains wash through local latrines and other waste.

Angola and Kavango. But fears of reduced and changed patterns of flow are indeed warranted because so much of the river system's functioning depends on regular strong flows and flooding that, for example, carry sediments into the Delta and enable fish to breed in floodplains. The variety of habitats in the Delta is largely the result of changing water levels, mainly because different plant communities occupy different flood zones.

The whole river system is characterized by low nutrients. Greater levels of nutrients, for instance in the form of nitrogen and phosphorous fertilizers washing out of large agricultural projects, would lead to more biological production, particularly in the Delta where the extra nutrients would accumulate. Beds of papyrus might expand, causing channels to close more quickly and rapid changes to the distribution of water. It is also likely that the abundance of Kariba weed, *Salvinia molesta*, would increase. This could have severe consequences for the Delta, since the weed forms dense mats covering large surface areas of calm water. The mats cause a reduction in the water's oxygen content.

Higher levels of other chemicals, such as calcium, magnesium, sodium and silica, would probably accompany nutrient increases. In this case, a severe reduction in papyrus could result from concentrations of these harmful solutes. Patterns of sediment accumulation and the way in which water is distributed in the Delta could change, habitat diversity may decrease, and the Delta might gradually change from a freshwater to a saline wetland. Levels of pollution from urban effluent and other sources are evidently negligible, but every effort needs to be made to safeguard the river from these and other toxic chemicals, such as pesticides. It is widely agreed that Botswana's use of endosulphan to kill tsetse flies reduced fish stocks in the Delta between the 1970s and early 1990s.

Angola considered the construction of hydroelectric schemes at 17 sites during the 1960s **(Figure 51)** but none of these have been developed. However, Namibia's announcement in 2003 that it intended to develop a similar scheme near Popa Falls elicited much alarm and criticism. The most important environmental fear to emerge during an initial impact assessment of the Popa scheme was the possible reduction in sediment movement because a dam would slow the speed of water flow. Sand washed down the river accumulates and raises bed levels in the Delta's channels, and this leads to channel switching once water levels rise (see page 91). The changes result in new areas being flooded, again contributing to the diversity of flood levels, plant communities and animal life.

Finally, Kavango has lost most of the natural plant life in the southern river valley, while the larger Angolan towns are surrounded by swathes of land cleared for crops (see the image on page 16). Many trees have also been killed for fuel wood and charcoal production in Angola, while soil erosion has increased as a result of land clearing and the creation of paths to the water. It is hard to argue that vegetation should be preserved if rural farmers need crops and fuel, but care should be taken in promoting policies and practices that lead to unsustainable use of these resources. It is so often argued that social and economic conditions can be improved by rural development, especially through small-scale farming. However, farming can only be profitable in the Basin under exceptional circumstances, and most small-scale farming practices are damaging to the environment. More importantly, most people will remain poor as small-scale farmers because farming conditions in the Basin are so limited and the lack of markets restricts the selling of surplus produce. Indeed, it is not surprising that so many people turn their backs on farming, rural livelihoods and poverty by moving to towns.

Taken individually, most of these different pressures now have little effect on the river. However, the cumulative effects may be considerable, especially along the Namibian section. Densities of people and cattle are highest here, most natural vegetation has been lost, and soil erosion is greatest. There are also several agricultural schemes that draw off water and from which pollutant chemicals and nutrients might be washed into the Okavango. All indications are that such pressures will increase as Namibia increasingly aims to use the river for irrigation, urban water supplies and hydroelectric power.

The frequent burning of large areas of natural vegetation (see page 111) has substantial consequences on the availability of pastures, swamp vegetation, woodlands and valuable timber species, and on soil nutrients.

Opportunities

The Okavango thus faces several kinds of pressures. Perhaps the biggest challenge, however, is that it is so difficult to achieve consensus on how the Okavango should be used and managed, and what its future might be. This is because there are so many differences in the use of resources and perspectives on the value of the river. Angolans use the river mainly for crops, drinking and washing, while in Namibia the river is used largely for watering and grazing livestock, Rundu's water supply, irrigating fields and to provide building materials and fish. In Botswana, the main uses are for tourism and building materials. Scales of use and interest also differ, from those of individual rural households to tribal communities, regional administrations, national governments and the international community. The three countries see the river differently: Angola is rich in water, and the catchment area is not a priority. Namibia has little water and as a temporary custodian of the river sees the passing flow as an opportunity not to let pass. Botswana, too, has little water, and has invested heavily to extract high profits from the Okavango, and has no intention of losing its investment or future income. Sharing water among so many different needs and perceptions is not easy.

Another severe problem is that the Okavango is less important to the governments of Angola, Namibia and Botswana than we might assume. First, the Basin is remote from their capitals and economic centres – out of sight, out of mind. Second, the Okavango offers each country little in the way of food or hydroelectric power (this could change for Namibia if its planned developments go ahead). Third, there are no known mineral resources to provide governments or politicians with good incomes. Finally, too few people live in the Basin to make the area politically important (see page 126). All of this is negative – perhaps cynical – but the reality is that governments are unlikely to pay much attention to the Okavango.

But there are many people who would like to see a secure future for the Okavango River system, a future in which water, sediments and nutrients continue to move down the network of rivers unhindered, for example. There is also the hope that resources are used on a sustainable basis, so that present generations treat the natural environment in ways that do not jeopardize the options of future generations. How might this be achieved? We offer several suggestions to conclude this journey down the Okavango.

A first step is to enlarge the Okavango's constituency of supporters. The Basin should mean more to many more people. The range of benefits derived from the rivers' natural resources has to be increased, and greater value must be attached to areas upstream of the Delta, for example through tourism. This is a particular challenge in Angola and Namibia where the number of supporters of the river is small. By contrast, backing and acclaim for the river is much greater in Botswana because of the substantial gains from the Delta. But even here there is a need to broaden the support base. Progress has been made by promoting community-based management and profit sharing from wildlife-based tourism to bring benefits to rural people. However, they have little official or political influence, and there is a challenge to involve wealthier, more influential citizens. The biggest challenge, of course, is to promote benefits derived from the careful management and use of natural resources across a broad spectrum of Angolan society.

Secondly, land in the Basin should be managed more effectively. Most land in the Basin is now communal or tribal land, such that no one owns land or takes responsibility for the resources it offers. Mechanisms that enable people to obtain long-term, tangible benefits from land are also lacking in most places. Botswana offers useful experience in its attempts to move from a system of common, open access to one of private property management. Tribal chiefs and headmen managed land tenure up until 1970, when land boards took over as trustees over tribal lands. The boards now allocate land for residential purposes and dry-land crop farming, and may cancel land rights and restrict certain land uses. Much of the land in and around the Delta has been designated as wildlife management areas in which the use and conservation of wildlife is the primary land use. Wildlife management areas in tribal areas can be leased as controlled hunting areas to recognized community groups. The leases are for nominal amounts, and the groups may earn substantial incomes by negotiating contracts with safari operators to use their areas for tourism or big game hunting.[4]

The key element behind controlled hunting areas is that communities are given long-term rights over wildlife and the opportunity to benefit from these resources. This helps boost the value of wildlife and hence the Basin area in which the animals live. Attempts are now being made to establish conservancies in several places along the Cubango/Okavango River in Kavango. Since there is very little wildlife in these areas, community involvement is rather aimed at improving and securing the management of scarce or depleted resources, such as fish, woodlands and pastures.

Almost the only interest in the Okavango ever expressed by the Namibian and Angolan governments is for irrigation, water supply and hydroelectric power schemes. There is room for such developments, but we believe the scope to be limited, and extreme care must be taken to restrict environmental damage. More importantly, and as a third recommendation, alternative uses of the Basin should be sought for Angola and Namibia. The most logical is to greatly expand the tourism industry upstream from the Delta. Indeed, there is scope for developing (and marketing) the whole Basin as a massive destination for international tourists. Wildlife attractions are now limited in most areas of Angola and Kavango, but there is much to offer in scenic beauty, fishing, remoteness and historical interest. The upper reaches of the Cuito and Cuanavale rivers appear to support fair numbers of wildlife, and populations throughout the catchment should increase as a result of protection.

The development of the Okavango catchment in south-eastern Angola as a major tourism attraction would improve livelihoods and safeguard the area's pristine environment.

Tourism in the Basin could complement nearby tourist attractions, such as Chobe, Victoria Falls and Etosha. The development of accommodation and attractions along the river in Kavango would also link tourism to the Okavango with Etosha and the many other well-developed destinations in north-western Namibia. Visitors could thus move between these broader areas on more extended visits. Developing tourism in south-eastern Angola will be challenging because

*Each one of the hundreds of tanks (above) now
strewn around south-eastern Angola probably cost
roughly the same as an up market lodge in Botswana
that now attracts wealthy tourists (inset) from around
the world: millions of dollars wasted upstream but
used wisely downstream. Each of the thousands of
missiles produced and blown to oblivion by some of
the world's most sophisticated armies cost many times
the amount paid to teachers and nurses each year.
Likewise, how many well-equipped schools and clinics
could have been built with the dollars paid for each jet
fighter that now lies wrecked in Angola? One may only
hope that governments will spend money more wisely
in the future so that people in the Okavango have
decent lives and that lechwe (opposite) continue to run
wild through the waters of the Okavango.*

the area is so remote and poorly served with
infrastructure. However, access by air and by boat
along the main rivers is relatively easy. The most
logical people to spearhead these developments are
safari and lodge operators from Botswana. They would
bring valuable experience to the area. By having
investments at both ends (so to speak) of the
Okavango, they would also have incentives to promote
the overall value of the river system.

Finally, most assessments of environmental concerns
in the Basin have focused on individual developments,
such as the Popa Falls hydroelectric scheme or the
pumping of water to Windhoek. Each of these small
projects is unlikely to have a major impact on the
Okavango. Rather, it is the cumulative effects of water
uses that are the real problem: of water lost here and
there, pollutants added in different places, or new rural
settlements, for example. We therefore suggest that
planning of a more strategic nature is really needed to
ensure the long-term health of the river system. Such

planning requires an overall assessment of the
Okavango that recognizes the widely differing views
and values that people in different parts of the Basin
hold. The assessment should highlight comparative
advantages and benefits offered at different places and
to different people or land uses.

All three countries should contribute to such an
assessment, and the results should be developed into
a management instrument that becomes binding on
all participants. This might be achieved through
government ratification of an agreement that upholds

the Okavango as an asset to be administered and developed as a single, ecological unit. Several treaties and conventions now offer frameworks for sharing water and managing river basins, but none are strong enough to force the three countries to manage the Basin co-operatively and wisely.[5] Angola, Namibia and Botswana also formed the Permanent Okavango River Basin Water Commission (OKACOM) in 1994 to promote the joint management of the Basin. More specifically, OKACOM was intended to advise the governments on sustainable development, to co-ordinate investigations and research, to share information and to prevent environmental damage. However, the Commission needs considerable strengthening – both technically and strategically – to perform these functions.

Two groups seem best placed to spearhead and promote a unified view of the Basin as a healthy unit. The first is the international community, perhaps through donors who formulate assistance to promote the sustainable use of natural resources throughout the Okavango. The second is the government and tourism industry in Botswana, where investments and profits from the use of the Okavango have been greatest. Although Botswana has made mistakes, it has also accumulated considerable experience in the wise management of the river, and it should consider sharing its experience and benefits with Namibia and Angola. Botswana also has most to lose if the Okavango's health fails.

In Botswana, there are usually screams of horror whenever an irrigation scheme, pipeline or dam is planned. By contrast, viewpoints upstream are such that most people in Angola and Namibia may not care how much water reaches the downstream Delta. Both perspectives – at either end of the Basin – need to change. Most thoughts on co-operation between Angola, Namibia and Botswana concentrate on how

water can be shared. This is to be expected, but it would also be useful to improve the debate to see how *benefits* can be shared. Most importantly, there is a need to shift away from the assumption that most benefits will come from agriculture and rural development. Changing these perspectives and assumptions is a great challenge. It is our hope that this book will go some way towards promoting a useful vision and bright future for the Okavango lifeline.

Key points

- Although the Okavango is generally in good environmental health, pressures come from water abstraction, changes to water and sediment flow, pollution and changes to nutrient levels, loss of vegetation, soil erosion and fires.
- Pressures on the river are much higher along the Namibian section than elsewhere, and they are likely to increase as a result of development plans and land uses in Namibia.
- Uses and values attached to the river vary greatly between the three countries and different users.
- The Okavango's future and sustainable use of resources should be safeguarded by enlarging its constituency of supporters, improving the management of land, and developing better use of its resources (especially through wildlife-based tourism).
- The Okavango should be managed as far as possible as a single, integrated ecological unit. Initiatives to adopt such an approach to its management should come from the international community and Botswana.

NOTES AND SOURCES

1. Introduction: the flow of a lifeline

1. Strictly speaking, the administrative district is called the North-West District, which is divided into Chobe, Ngamiland East, Ngamiland West, and Okavango sub-districts. However, the area shown as Ngamiland in Figure 1 is widely recognized as a district and many sets of statistical information are collected for this separate area.

2. Landscapes: the shape of a river

1. This account is based on information provided by Roger Swart, and also by John Ward and Brian Bluck. Important references are: Partridge, T.C. 1998. Of diamonds, dinosaurs and diastrophism: 150 million years of landscape evolution in southern Africa. *South African Journal of Geology*. 101: 167–184; Gumbricht, T., McCarthy, T.S. & Merry, C.L. 2001. The topography of the Okavango Delta, Botswana, and its tectonic and sedimentological implications. *South African Journal of Geology*. 104: 243–264; Thomas, D.S.G. & Shaw, P.A. 1991. *The Kalahari Environment*. Cambridge University Press, Cambridge.

2. Derived from maps produced by the Council for Geosciences in South Africa, the Geological Survey or Namibia and the Instituto Nacional de Geologia, Angola. Dunes were traced off satellite images. Basalts and volcanics associated with the breakup of Gondwana (e.g. Karoo basalts and Etendeka lavas) have been included in the Karoo Group. For discussions on the ages of dunes see Thomas, D.S.G. & Shaw, P.A. 2002. Late Quaternary environmental change in central southern Africa: new data, synthesis, issues and prospects. *Quaternary Science Reviews* 21: 783–797.

3. Moore, A.E. & Larkin, P.A. 2001. Drainage evolution in south-central Africa since the breakup of Gondwana. *South African Journal of Geology* 104: 47–68.

4. Same as 3.

5. Sophie Simmonds helped compile the information, which was based on InterConsult. 2001. *Natural resource mapping of the Kavango*. Report for the Directorate of Environmental Affairs, Windhoek; Castanheira Diniz, A. & De Barros Aguiar, F.Q. 1973. *Recursos em terras com Aptidão para o regadio na Bacia do Cubango*. Instituto de Investigação Agronomica de Angola. No 33; and data compiled by the Ministry of Agriculture, Gaborone.

3. The past: trying times

1. Robbins, L.H. & Murphy, M.L. 1998. The Early and Middle Stone Age. In Lane, P., Reid, A. & Segobye, A. (eds). *Ditswa Mmung: The archaeology of Botswana*. Pula Press and The Botswana Society, Gaborone.

2. From Baum, H. 1903. *Kunene-Sambesi Expedition*. Kolonial Wirtschaftliches Komitee. Berlin.

3. From information in Lane, P., Reid, A. & Segobye, A. (eds). 1998. *Ditswa Mmung: The archaeology of Botswana*. Pula Press and The Botswana Society, Gaborone for Botswana and provided by John Kinahan for Angola and Namibia.

4. Compiled from Milheiros, M. 1967. *Notas de etnografia Angolana*. Instituto de Investigação Cientifica de Angola; Redinha, J. 1962. *Distribuição etnica de Angola*. Edição Do Centro de Informação e turismo de Angola; Robins, S., Madzudzo, E. & Brenzinger. M. 2001. *An assessment of the status of the San in South Africa, Angola, Zambia and Zimbabwe*. Legal Assistance Centre, Windhoek; Cassidy, L., Good, K., Mazonde, I. & Rivers, R. 2001. An assessment of the status of the San in Botswana. Legal Assistance Centre, Windhoek; Bendsen, H. 2002.

Arable Agriculture and its significance in terms of spatial coverage, job and income generation potential. Unpublished report, Harry Oppenheimer Okavango Research Centre, Maun; Mendelsohn, J.M. & el Obeid, S. 2003. *Sand and water: a profile of the Kavango Region in Namibia*. Struik, Cape Town.

5. Nettelton, G.E., 1934. *History of the Ngamiland Tribes up to 1926*. Bantu Studies 8.

6. Sillery, A. 1952. *The Bechuanaland Protectorate*. Oxford University Press, Cape Town.

7. MPLA: Popular Movement for the Liberation of Angola, FNLA: National Front for the Liberation of Angola and UNITA: National Union for the Total Independence of Angola.

4. Climate: driving rains, drying sunshine

1. Based on an interpolation of average seasonal totals calculated from records obtained from the Global Historical Climate Network database, and the Botswana and Namibia Meteorological Services.

2. Ministry of Finance and Development Planning. 1997. *Study of poverty and poverty alleviation in Botswana*. Gaborone.

3. Based on an interpolation of the standard deviation of annual totals calculated from records obtained from the sources in Note 1. The coefficient is the standard deviation of annual totals as a percentage of the average rainfall each year.

4. From sources in Note 1.

5. These figures are for an area near Pretoria in South Africa, but the cycles approximate those in the Basin at the same time. Adapted from Tyson, P.D. & Preston-Whyte, R.A. 1998. T*he weather and climate of southern Africa*. Oxford University Press, Cape Town.

6. From the Botswana and Namibia Meteorological Services.

7. Data from Namibia Meteorological Services: Marques, R. 1998. *Climate, hydrology and water resources: Angolan sector*. Report for OKACOM Diagnostic Assessment. GEF Project Brief; and Wilson. B.H. & Dincer, T. 1976. An introduction to the hydrology and hydrography of the Okavango Delta. In: *Proceedings of the symposium on the Okavango Delta and its future utilization*. Botswana Society, Gaborone.

5. The River: meandering across the Kalahari

1. Thomas, D.S.G. & Shaw, P.A. 1991. *The Kalahari environment*. Cambridge University Press, Cambridge.

2. Catchment areas were mapped and their sizes calculated by this project. Average rainfall was estimated from interpolated mean annual rainfall figures in each catchment (see page 63). Multiplying average rainfall and catchment areas provided estimates of total volumes of rainfall per catchment. Discharge percentages are the proportions of rainfall volume per catchment relative to the total volume of rainfall over the whole active catchment area. Note that summing the percentages in the table results in an estimated 60% of total flow from the Cubango sub-Basin and 40% from the Cuito sub-Basin, slightly different from the proportions recorded at gauging stations of 55% for the Cubango and 45% for the Cuito.

3. Of the 22% coming down the Cuito, 15% is from its own catchment and 7% collects after its junction with the Cuanavale. Similarly, of the 14% inflow to the Cubango, 9% is from its own catchment, while the remaining 5% drains into the river below its junctions with the Cutato, Cuchi, Cacuchi, Cuelei and Cuebe.

4. The figure of 9.4 cubic kilometres was calculated from all measurements of discharge at Mohembo over the past 68 years. The estimate of 3.2 cubic kilometres of rainwater (Fred Ellery, personal communication) is lower than other published figures, perhaps because other workers over-estimated the area of swamps.

5. McCarthy, T.S., Bloem, A. & Larkin P.A. 1998. Observations on the hydrology and geohydrology of the Okavango Delta. *South African Journal of Geology* 101: 101–117.

6. Some additional water may be added from the underground flow of water from aquifers in the Kavango (Mendelsohn, J.M. & el Obeid, S. 2003. *Sand and Water: a profile of the Kavango Region in Namibia*. Struik, Cape Town). The amounts of water are unknown, but are unlikely to contribute significantly to river flow.

7. Based on data recorded at gauging stations at different places given in Marques, R. 1998. *Climate, hydrology and water resources: Angolan sector*. Report for OKACOM Diagnostic Assessment. GEF Project Brief., and by the Department of Water Affairs in Namibia and Botswana. The flow of the Okavango (before the Cuito) and the Cuito was compared by subtracting flow at Mohembo from that at Rundu.

8. From data supplied by the Department of Water Affairs in Botswana and Namibia.

9. McCarthy, J., Gumbricht, T., McCarthy, T., Frost, P. Wessels, K. & Siedel, F. Flooding patterns of the Okavango Wetland in Botswana between 1972 and 2000. Submitted to *Ambio*.

10. Same as 5.

11. Same as 8.

12. Adapted from McCarthy, J. 2002. *Remote sensing for detection of landscape form and function of the Okavango Delta, Botswana*. Ph D. thesis. Royal Institute of Technology, Stockholm.

13. Gumbricht, T., McCarthy, J. & McCarthy, T.S. In press. Channels, wetlands and islands in the Okavango Delta, Botswana, and their relation to hydrological and sedimentological processes. *Earth Surface Processes and Landforms*.

14. More information can be found in: Ellery, W.N., Ellery, K., Rogers, K.H., McCarthy, T.S. & Walker, B.H, 1993. Vegetation, hydrology and sedimentation processes as determinants of channel form and dynamics in the northeastern Okavango Delta, Botswana. *African Journal of Ecology* 31: 10–25.

15. Garstang, M., Ellery, W.N., McCarthy, T.S., Scholes, M.C., Scholes, R.J., Swap, R.J. & Tyson, P.D. 1998. The contribution of aerosol- and water-borne nutrients to the functioning of the Okavango Delta ecosystem, Botswana. *South African Journal of Science* 94: 223–229.

6. Living resources: the Okavango's plants and animals

1. Important publications on fish are: Hay, C.J., van Zyl, B.J. & Steyn, G.J. 1996. A quantitative assessment of the biotic integrity of the Okavango River, Namibia based on fish. *Water SA* 22: 263–284; Van der Waal, B.C.W. 1991. A survey of the fisheries in the Kavango, Namibia. *Madoqua* 17: 113–122; and Mosepele, K. 2002. *Trends in fisheries development and fish utilization in the Okavango Delta*. Unpublished report, Harry Oppenheimer Okavango Research Centre, Maun.

2. Based on Hay, C.J.1995. *The development of a database for the assessment of the biotic integrity and sustainable utilisation of the Okavango River, Namibia*. Ph D. Thesis, Rand Afrikaans University, Johannesburg; Fox, P.J. 1976. Preliminary observations on fish communities of the Okavango Delta. In *Proceedings of the symposium on the Okavango Delta and its future utilization*. Botswana Society, Gaborone.

3. Van der Waal, B.C.W. 1991. A survey of the fisheries in the Kavango, Namibia. *Madoqua* 17: 113–122; Tvedten, I., Girvan, L-A., Maasdorp, M., Pomuti, A. & Van Rooy, G. 1994. *Freshwater fisheries and fish management in Namibia: A socio-economic background study*. Social Sciences Division, University of Namibia, Windhoek; Income and Expenditure

Survey of 1994, conducted by the Namibian Central Statistics Office; and extrapolations in Mendelsohn, J.M. & el Obeid, S. 2003. *Sand and water: a profile of the Kavango Region in Namibia*. Struik, Cape Town.

4. Tvedten, I., Girvan, L-A., Maasdorp, M., Pomuti, A. & Van Rooy, G. 1994. *Freshwater fisheries and fish management in Namibia: A socio-economic background study*. Social Sciences Division, University of Namibia, Windhoek.

5. Mosepele, K. 2002. *Trends in Fisheries Development and Fish Utilization in the Okavango Delta*. Unpublished report, Harry Oppenheimer Okavango Research Centre, Maun.

6. Same as 5.

7. Same as 5. Figures amount to more than 100% because some people use more than one method.

8. Same as 5.

9. Louis du Pisani analyzed NOAA NDVI satellite data to produce these maps. Data from 1993/94 and 1994/95 were not available.

10. Map and text based on: Dos Santos, R. M. 1982. *Itinerários floristicos e carta de vegetação do Cuando Cubango. Estudos, ensaios e documentos* 137. Instituto de Investigação Cientifica Tropical, Junta de Investigações Cientificas do Ultramar, Lisbon; Smith, P.A. 1976. An outline of the vegetation of the Okavango drainage system. In *Proceedings of the symposium on the Okavango Delta and its future utilization*. Botswana Society, Gaborone; Ellery, W.N., McCarthy, T. & Dangerfield, W.J. 2000. Floristic diversity in the Okavango Delta, Botswana as an endogenous product of biological activity. *Biodiversity in wetlands: assessment, function and conservation*. Vol. 1. Backhuys Publishers, Leiden; and our interpretation of satellite images.

11. Jones, B.T.B. 2001. *Results of a socio-ecological survey carried out in the Kavango Region, Namibia, May–August 2001*. Report for the Every River has its People project, Windhoek.

12. Data provided by Alex Verlinden, National Remote Sensing Centre, Windhoek.

13. From the Botswana Department of Wildlife and National Parks reports on aerial surveys.

14. Figures summarized by Mendelsohn, J.M. & el Obeid, S. 2003. *Sand and water: a profile of the Kavango Region in Namibia*. Struik, Cape Town.

15. Mbaiwa. J.E. 2002. *The socio-economic and environmental impact of tourism development in the Okavango Delta, Botswana*. Harry Oppenheimer Okavango Research Centre, Maun.

16. From records kept at Popa Game Park.

17. Note 15 and Scott Wilson Resource Consultants. 2000. *Environmental assessment of veterinary fences in Ngamiland*. Report for the Government of Botswana.

7. People: change and motion

1. Based on the total estimated population in the Basin area of each country as a percentage of the national population, taken as 13 million for Angola, 1.9 million for Namibia and 1.7 million for Botswana. The map is based on Morebodi, B.B.H. 2001. *Botswana National Atlas*. Department of Surveys and Mapping, Gaborone; and Namibian 2000 Demographic and Health Survey; Mendelsohn, J.M., Jarvis, A.M., Roberts, C.S. & Robertson, T. 2002. *Atlas of Namibia*. David Philip, Cape Town; and UNEP database of population density in Angola (grid2.cd.usgs.gov/globalpop/Africa).

2. Densities in Kavango were from Mendelsohn, J.M. & el Obeid, S. 2003. *Sand and water: a profile of the Kavango Region in Namibia*. Struik, Cape Town. For Ngamiland, numbers of people recorded in the 2001 census were 'spread' over distances of five kilometres around each village. For Angola, we used population estimates for different towns supplied by OCHA (Office for Co-ordination of Humanitarian Affairs), our own estimates of village sizes from aerial and ground surveys and density estimates from the UNEP database of population densities for certain

areas. These sources provided a total estimate of about 370,000 people in Angola. In addition, from areas cleared for cultivation (mapped off recent satellite images) and our assumption that an average household of five people had cleared 10 hectares, a total population of 320,000 people in Angola is estimated. We are thus fairly confident that the real total is unlikely to be less than 300,000 or more than 400,000 people. Official estimates of populations in Angola are far too high, a consequence of how the central government allocates funds to each province on the basis of the number of people claimed by each province.

3. Population figures for Kavango and Ngamiland are for the whole region or district from government population censuses.

4. Populations on the north bank were 35% of those in Kavango in 1940, 40% in 1950, and 46% in 1960. From Gibson, G.D., Larson, T.J. & McGurk, C.R. 1981. *The Kavango Peoples*. Franz Steiner Verlag, Wiesbaden.

5. Namibian 2000 Demographic and Health Survey and Morebodi, B.B.H. 2001. *Botswana National Atlas*. Department of Surveys and Mapping, Gaborone.

6. For several accounts see Pacheco, F. 2001. Rural communities in Huambo. In Robson, P. (ed.). *Communities and reconstruction in Angola*. Occasional Paper No. 1 of the Development Workshop, Guelph, Canada.

7. Based on sources listed in Note 4, chapter 3 on history.

8. Porto, J.G. & Clover, J. 2002. *The peace divided in Angola: strategic implications for the Okavango Basin cooperation*. Report for African Security Analysis Programme, Institute of Security Studies; World Health Organization Indicators for 2001 (www3.who.int).

9. From discussions with various people in Menongue in May 2003.

10. From Sentinel Surveys conducted and reported by the Botswana and Namibia Ministry of Health. A sentinel survey was not done in 2000 in Ngamiland.

11. Combined schools offer some primary and secondary grades. Information from Morebodi, B.B.H. 2001. *Botswana National Atlas*. Department of Surveys and Mapping, Gaborone; el Obeid, S., Mendelsohn, J.M., Lejars, M., Forster, N. & Brulé, G. *Health in Namibia: progress and challenges*. RAISON, Windhoek; Ministry of Basic Education, Sport and Culture in Namibia and Harry Oppenheimer Okavango Research Centre, Maun.

12. See Mendelsohn, J.M. & el Obeid, S. 2003. *Sand and water: a profile of the Kavango Region in Namibia*. Struik, Cape Town.

13. From World Health Organization indicators for 2001 (www3.who.int); the Namibian 2000 Demographic and Health Survey; and Morebodi, B.B.H. 2001. *Botswana National Atlas*. Department of Surveys and Mapping, Gaborone.

8. Farming: food, income and security

1. These estimates are based on average household sizes and the density of people in rural areas within the Basin (see page 126).

2. New irrigation projects are in accordance with Namibia's 'Green Scheme' to promote food production and security. The projects will be large commercial enterprises that support groups of nearby small-scale irrigation farm units.

3. Bendsen, H. 2002. *The dynamics of the land use systems in Ngamiland*. Unpublished report, Harry Oppenheimer Okavango Research Centre, Maun.

4. Data from Kavango analyzed from the Population Survey of the Kavango Region by Lux Development in 1999, while that for Ngamiland comes from Van Hoof, P.J.M., Kirkels, M.A.L.J., Riezebos, H.Th., Schledorn, J.L.M. & de Wit, M.J.M. 1991. *Socio-economic baseline survey and land suitability analysis of Ngamiland district CSDA, Western part*. University of Utrecht.

5. Van Hoof *et al.* (see Note 4) and Rashem, K. 1988. *Economic findings and results: dryland and molapo farming systems of western Ngamiland*. Technical Report No.5. Department of Agricultural Research, Ministry of Agriculture, Botswana.

6. Ministry of Finance and Development Planning. 1997. *Study of poverty and poverty alleviation in Botswana*. Gaborone.

7. Mendelsohn, J.M. & el Obeid, S. 2003. *Sand and water: a profile of the Kavango Region in Namibia*. Struik, Cape Town; and Kgathi, D.L. 2003. *Natural resources tenure and access in the Okavango Delta*. Unpublished report, Harry Oppenheimer Okavango Research Centre, Maun.

8. Mendelsohn, J.M. & el Obeid, S. 2003. *Sand and water: a profile of the Kavango Region in Namibia*. Struik, Cape Town.

9. Same as 8.

10. For Angola, yields are reported by Borchert, G. 1963. *Südost-Angola*. Institut für Geographie und Wirtschaftsgeographie der Universität. Hamburg. In Kavango, yields are given by: Keyler, S. 1995. *Economics of the pearl millet subsector in northern Namibia. A summary of baseline data.* International Crops Research Institute for the Semi-Arid Tropics. *Working Paper 95/03.* Anon. 1997. *Farm management survey of the Okavango Region, Analysis Report 1.* Ministry of Agriculture, Water and Rural Development, and Yaron, G., Janssen, G & Maamberua, U. 1992. *Rural Development in the Okavango Region of Namibia: An Assessment of Needs, Opportunities and Constraints.* Windhoek, Gamsberg Macmillan. For Ngamiland, yields are reviewed by Bendsen, H. 2002. *The dynamics of the land use systems in Ngamiland.* Unpublished report, Harry Oppenheimer Okavango Research Centre, Maun.

11. Rashem, K. 1988. *Economic findings and results: dryland and molapo farming systems of western Ngamiland.* Technical Report No.5. Department of Agricultural Research, Ministry of Agriculture, Botswana.

12. For a fuller argument see Mendelsohn, J.M. & el Obeid, S. 2003. *Sand and water: a profile of the Kavango Region in Namibia.* Struik, Cape Town.

13. Figures for Angola are guesses based on our observations that only a small proportion of farmers own cattle, their herds are generally small, and there are very few cattle in the northern half of the catchment, even though there are many more farmers in the northern areas. Similar points are made by Borchert, G. 1963. *Südost-Angola.* Institut für Geographie und Wirtschaftsgeographie der Universität. Hamburg. For Kavango, there are about 150,000 cattle in the Kavango region, but roughly 90,000 of these are on farms beyond 20 kilometres from the river. The estimate of 50,000 cattle within 20 kilometres of the Delta is based on there being about 8,500 rural households in the area, each of which would have about six cattle. Most other cattle in Ngamiland are at cattle posts and on farms to the west and south of the Delta. Similar methods were used to estimate numbers of goats.

14. For Ngamiland, figures are from Van Hoof *et al* (see Note 4); while for Kavango data are from a Population Survey of the Kavango Region by Lux Development in 1999. The ownership of goats seems low in Ngamiland and more recent figures may show that more households have goats.

15. From census and vaccination campaign figures of the Directorate of Veterinary Services in Namibia and Agricultural Planning and Statistics of the Ministry of Agriculture, Central Statistics Office, Gaborone.

16. For Angola, derived from an estimate of cattle distribution relative to the distribution of rural farmers (see page 127), for Kavango from Mendelsohn, J.M. & el Obeid, S. 2003. *Sand and water: a profile of the Kavango Region in Namibia.* Struik, Cape Town, and for Ngamiland from Scott Wilson Resource Consultants. 2000. *Environmental assessment of veterinary fences in Ngamiland.* Report for the Government of Botswana.

17. Estimates for Kavango are based on annual Meatco sales of about 2,500 head and extrapolations from Kirsten, J. 1999. *Livestock marketing study.* Report for Northern Regions Livestock Development Project (NOLIDEP), Windhoek, while figures for Ngamiland are reported by Scott Wilson Resource Consultants. 2000. *Environmental assessment of veterinary fences in Ngamiland.* Report for the Government of Botswana.

18. Same as 8.

19. Andersson, C.J. 1861. *The Okavango River. A narrative of travel, exploration and adventure.* London.

20. Same as 8.

21. Social Impact Assessment and Policy Analysis Corporation (SIAPAC). 2001. *Rural Development Policy Review Nationwide Consultations*. Botswana Institute for Development Policy Analysis (BIDPA), Gaborone, Botswana.

22. Keyler, S. 1995. Economics of the pearl millet subsector in northern Namibia. A summary of baseline data. *International Crops Research Institute for the Semi-Arid Tropics*. Working Paper 95/03.

23. Fidzani, B., Mlenga, W.S., Atlhopheng, M. & Shatera, M.M. 1999. *Socio-economic effects of CBPP in Ngamiland*. Ministry of Agriculture, Gaborone.

24. Income and Expenditure Survey of 1994, Central Statistics Office, Namibia.

9. Okavango: opportunities and challenges

1. Mendelsohn, J.M. & el Obeid, S. 2003. *Sand and water: a profile of the Kavango Region in Namibia*. Struik, Cape Town.

2. Information from the Namibian Department of Water Affairs. There are also more tentative plans to develop a further 2,000 ha at Kangongo, bringing the total area of irrigation there to 4,000 ha.

3. Previous estimates have put Namibia's use at 0.05% and Botswana's use at 0.04% of total flow into the Delta (see Ashton, P J. 2000. Water security for multi-national river basin states: The special case of the Okavango River. In Falkenmark, M & Lundqvist, J (eds). *2000 SIWI seminar – Water security for multi-national river basin states – Opportunity for development*. Stockholm: Swedish International Water Institute).

4. Kgathi, D.L. 2002. *Natural Resources Tenure and Access in the Okavango Delta*. Unpublished Report, Harry Oppenheimer Okavango Research Centre, Maun.

5. The following conventions, treaties and protocols are relevant: Ramsar Convention on Wetlands of International Importance, United Nations Convention on Biological Diversity, United Nations Convention to Combat Desertification, United Nations Convention on the Non-Navigational Uses of International Watercourses, United Nations Framework Convention on Climate Change, and Revised Protocol on Shared Watercourse Systems (SADC 2001). These are discussed in detail by Ashton, P. & Neal, M. 2003. An overview of key strategic issues in the Okavango basin. In Turton, T., Ashton, P. & Eugene Cloete, E. (eds). 2003. *Transboundary rivers, sovereignty and development: hydropolitical drivers in the Okavango River basin*. African Water Issues Research Unit, Pretoria and Green Cross International, Geneva.

Important References

1. Barnes, J., Cannon, J. & Morrison, K. 2001. *Economic returns to selected land uses in Ngamiland, Botswana*. Conservation International.

2. Baum, H. 1903. *Kunene-Sambesi Expedition*. Kolonial Wirtschaftliches Komitee. Berlin.

3. Bendsen, H. 2002. *The dynamics of the land use systems in Ngamiland*. Harry Oppenheimer Okavango Research Centre, Maun.

4. Bendsen, H. 2002. *Arable Agriculture and its significance in terms of spatial coverage, job and income generation potential*. Harry Oppenheimer Okavango Research Centre, Maun.

5. Bethune, S. 1991. Kavango River wetlands. *Madoqua* 17: 77–112.

6. Borchert, G. 1963. *Südost-Angola*. Institut für Geographie und Wirtschaftsgeographie der Universität. Hamburg.

7. Castanheira Diniz, A. & De Barros Aguiar, F.Q. 1973. *Recursos em terras com Aptidão para o regadio na Bacia do Cubango*. Instituto de Investigação Agronomica de Angola. No 33.

8. Dos Santos, R. M. 1982. *Itinerários floristicos e carta de vegetação do Cuando Cubango. Estudos, ensaios e documentos* 137. Instituto de Investigação Cientifica Tropical, Junta de Investigações Cientificas do Ultramar, Lisbon.

9. Ellery. W.N., Ellery. K., Rogers. K.H., McCarthy. T.S. & Walker B.H, 1993. Vegetation, hydrology and sedimentation processes as determinants of channel form and dynamics in the northeastern Okavango Delta, Botswana. *African Journal of Ecology* 31: 10–25.

10. Fidzani, B., Mlenga, W.S., Atlhopheng, M. & Shatera, M.M. 1999. *Socio-economic effects of CBPP in Ngamiland*. Ministry of Agriculture, Gaborone.

11. Fisch, M. 1984. Die Kavangofischer. *Namibiana* 5: 105–169.

12. Gibson, G.D, Larson, T.J. & McGurk, C.R. 1981. *The Kavango Peoples*. Franz Steiner Verlag, Wiesbaden.

13. Gumbricht, T., McCarthy, T.S. & Merry, C.L. 2001. The topography of the Okavango Delta, Botswana, and its tectonic and sedimentological implications. *South African Journal of Geology* 104: 243–264.

14. InterConsult. 2001. *Natural resource mapping of the Kavango*. Report for the Directorate of Environmental Affairs, Windhoek.

15. IUCN. 1992. *Angola: Environment status quo assessment report*. IUCN Regional Office for Southern Africa, Harare 1992.

16. Kgathi, D.L. 2003. *Natural resources tenure and access in the Okavango Delta*. Harry Oppenheimer Okavango Research Centre, Maun.

17. Lane, P., Reid, A. & Segobye, A. (eds). 1998. *Ditswa Mmung: The archaeology of Botswana*. Pula Press and The Botswana Society, Gaborone.

18. Mbaiwa. J.E. 2002. *The socio-economic and environmental impact of tourism development in the Okavango Delta, Botswana*. Harry Oppenheimer Okavango Research Centre, Maun.

19. McCarthy T.S., Bloem A., Larkin P.A. 1998. Observations of the hydrology and geohydrology of the Okavango Delta. *South African Journal of Geology*, 101: 101–117.

20. McCarthy, J. 2002. *Remote sensing for detection of landscape form and function of the Okavango Delta, Botswana*. Ph D. thesis. Royal Institute of Technology, Stockholm.

21. Mendelsohn, J.M., Jarvis, A.M., Roberts, C.S. & Robertson, T. 2002. *Atlas of Namibia*. David Philip, Cape Town.

22. Mendelsohn, J.M. & el Obeid, S. 2003. *Sand and water: a profile of the Kavango Region in Namibia*. Struik, Cape Town.

23. Merron, G.S. & Bruton, M.N. 1988. *The ecology and management of the fishes of the Okavango delta, Botswana with special reference to the role of the seasonal floods*. J.L.B. Smith Institute of Ichthyology Investigational Report No. 29. 291pp.

24. Ministry of Agriculture, Water and Rural Development. 1996. *Feasibility study on the Okavango River to Grootfontein link of the Eastern National Water Carrier*. 6 volumes. Windhoek.

25. Morebodi, B.B.H. 2001. *Botswana National Atlas*. Department of Surveys and Mapping, Gaborone.

26. Mosepele, K. 2002. *Trends in fisheries development and fish utilization in the Okavango Delta*. Harry Oppenheimer Okavango Research Centre, Maun.

27. Scott Wilson Resource Consultants. 2000. *Environmental assessment of veterinary fences in Ngamiland*. Report for the Government of Botswana.

28. Scudder, T. *et al.* 1992. *The IUCN review of Southern Okavango Integrated Water Development*. The World Conservation Union.

29. SMEC (Snowy Mountain Engineering Corporation). 1987–1991. Southern Okavango Integrated Water Development. Reports to the Department of Water Affairs, Gaborone.

30. Thomas, D.S.G. & Shaw, P.A. 1991. *The Kalahari Environment*. Cambridge University Press, Cambridge.

31. Turton, T. Ashton, P. & Eugene Cloete, E. (eds). 2003. *Transboundary rivers, sovereignty and development: hydropolitical drivers in the Okavango River basin*. African Water Issues Research Unit, Pretoria and Green Cross International, Geneva.

32. Van Hoof, P.J.M., Kirkels, M.A.L.J., Riezebos, H.Th., Schledorn, J.L.M. & de Wit, M.J.M. 1991. *Socio-economic baseline survey and land suitability analysis of Ngamiland district CSDA, Western part*. University of Utrecht.

33. Various authors. *Proceedings of the symposium on the Okavango Delta and its future utilization*, 1976. National Museum, Gaborone. Volume of papers on the Delta.

34. Various authors. 1987. *Journal of the South West African Scientific Society* 40/41: 29–45. Whole issue devoted to papers on the Kavango Region.

35. Various authors. 1998. Specialist reports for OKACOM (Permanent Okavango River Basin Commission) Diagnostic Assessments. GEF Project Brief.

36. White, R. 1993. *Livestock development and pastoral production on communal rangeland in Botswana*. The Botswana Society, Gaborone.

40. Yaron, G., Janssen, G & Maamberua, U. 1992. *Rural development in the Okavango Region of Namibia: an assessment of needs, opportunities and constraints*. Gamsberg Macmillan, Windhoek.

INDEX

possible effect on Delta 164
fires
  effect on environment 110–111, 165
  frequency and extent of 110–111
  peat 87
fish 96–100
  breeding areas 98
  low biomass 99
  communities 98
  species 96–97
fishing 96–100
flooding
  determining factors 84
  annual differences in 86
  largest extent 84
  passage of 85
Floodplain Valleys 79, 105
foods, staple 141
foot-and-mouth disease 152
Fossil Drainage Valleys 105
fossil rivers 77
fruits, household consumption of 108

G

geological origins 32
giraffe 117
goats 150–154
Gondwana 32, 33, 34
grass, uses of 108

H

habitats, diversity of 88, 91
health
  introduction of 54
  problems 135
  services 134–135
hippo 116
  effect on water flows 91
HIV infection rates 134
household incomes 156
human settlement
  early indications of 50
  patterns of 52–53, 127
hunting
  early 51
hydroelectric schemes 162, 165

I

immigration
  early 52
  effects of recent 129–130
impala 117
Incised Valleys 77–78
income
  farming as source of 156
  household 156
  from tourism 122
infrastructure
  development of 54, 162
  effect of civil war on 59
internally displaced people (IDPs) 131
irrigation schemes 44, 138, 162, 163

islands
  Andara islands 108
  role in concentrating salts 90

K

Kalahari Basin 36
Kalahari sand 43, 92, 160
Karoo rocks 32, 33
Kavango
  Region 29
  factors affecting farming 157
  social services 59
Kuando Kubango 29, 48

L

labour
  forced 54
  for farming 140–141,
Lake Ngami 35, 48, 87
land
  for crop production 145–148, 163
  management 166
  ownership 155
landmines 56, 59, 154
languages
  distributions 51, 132, 133
  groups 132–134
lechwe 29, 114
life expectancy 134
lifestyles, changing 126, 154
literacy 134
livestock (see cattle, goats)
lung sickness 150, 152

M

maize 141–143
Makgadikgadi Pan 36, 67, 73, 89
mammals, large 112–117
manioc 141, 144
migration 131
millet 141–144
mineral resources 37
missionaries 54
molapo fields 145–146
Mopane Woodlands 106

N

natural resources
  differences between countries 166
  impact on livelihoods 154
  importance of 26–27
  increasing the benefits of 166
  mineral 37
  plant 108–111
Ngamiland
  District 29
  factors affecting farming 157
  social services 59
nutrients
  abundance in Delta 93
  deficiency in soils 44
  deficiency in river water 93, 164

effect on swamp growth 90, 164
nuts, household consumption of 108

O

Okavango Basin
  definition of 17, 74
  extent of 72–73
OKACOM 169
onaka fields 145–146

P

Panhandle 79
Papyrus, effect on water speed 91
peat 87, 93
Permanent Swamps 80, 105–106
perspectives
  differences between countries 166
Planalto Grasslands 104
plants
  burning of 110
  communities 100–101
  diversity of 100–107
  levels of growth 90, 102
  role in reducing salts 90
  transpiration 77, 90
  uses of 108–111
planting seasons 142
population 126–132
  change in character 130
  densities 126–127
  displacement 52, 58, 129
  effect of change on 126
  growth 128–129
  movement of 52, 129, 130, 160
  proportion of young people 129
  structure 129, 130
poverty alleviation and rural development 156
pressures, on the environment 162

R

rainfall 62–67
  distribution 63
  historical changes 67
  seasonality 66, 142
  variation 64
reedbuck 118
refugees 129
relief 37–41
rift valley 32
rinderpest epidemic 123, 153
rivers
  catchments 74
  changing courses 36, 41, 77, 87
  names of 72
  gradients of 41
river flows
  annual 83
  fluctuation of 86
  historical flows 36
  importance of strong 98, 164
  peak 82
  rivers providing greatest 76–77

Sources of photographs and satellite images

A. Bailey: 47 / **H. Baum:** 49 (all) / **B. Curtis:** 80 (bottom), 146 (middle) / **H. Denker:** cover, 3 (left), 4 (right), 8 (middle), 10, 23 (middle & right), 31, 39, 41 (both), 42, 46, 50 (both), 51 (both), 55, 57, 58 (bottom), 61, 65 (both), 69, 71, 73, 75, 78, 79, 80 (top), 92 (both), 100, 101 (top), 105, 106 (bottom), 107 (bottom), 127, 130, 132 (middle), 135, 146 (top), 164 (top), 165 (top), 167 (bottom). / **M. Fisch:** 52 (bottom), 110 (left) / **A. Franca:** 56 (top) / **M. Harvey:** 27 (top), 28 (middle), 81 (bottom), 99 (right), 5, 155, 161, 169, 115 (top), 118 (bottom) / **HPH Photography:** 118 (top) / **Meteosat:** 62 / **NASA:** 16, 35, 37, 58 (top), 129, 107 (top) / **I. Michler:** 28 (top), 68, 103, 122 / **National Archives of Namibia:** 48, 53 (both), 54 / **A. Mertens:** 52 (top) / **M. Paxton:** 163 / **P. & B. Pickford:** 8 (left), 15 (bottom), 25, 29, 30, 67, 94, 96, 98, 99 (left), 106 (top), 109 (bottom), 112 (both), 113, 114 (both), 115 (bottom), 116 (both), 117 (both), 119 (both), 120 (all), 131, 137, 151 (bottom), 153, 158, 159, 176 (right). / **M. Picker:** 123 / **RAISON:** 2, 3 (right), 4 (left & middle), 11 (all), 12, 14, 15 (top), 23 (left), 26, 27 (bottom), 28 (bottom), 34, 43, 45, 56 (bottom), 60, 70, 76 (both), 81 (top), 84 (both), 85, 89, 90 (both), 91 (both), 97, 101 (bottom), 102, 108, 109 (top & middle), 110 (top & middle), 124, 125, 128, 132 (top & bottom), 133, 136, 139, 140, 141 (all), 142, 143 (bottom), 144 (all), 146 (bottom), 147, 148, 149 (both), 150 (both), 151 (top), 152, 164 (bottom), 167 (middle), 168 (top). 176 (left & middle), back flap (both)/ **D. Rogers:** 13, 121 / **J. Silva:** 56 (middle) / **P. Tarr:** front flap (top), 1, 3 (middle), 6, 24, 104, 167 (top) / **B. Terry:** front flap (bottom), 3 (top), 110 (bottom) / **P. Wagner:** 168 (bottom), inside flap (bottom).